C000058316

TEACHING MATHEMATICS AND ART

Edited by

Lesley Jones

Goldsmiths' College, University of London

STANLEY THORNES (Publishers) Ltd

First published in 1991 by:
Stanley Thornes (Publishers) Ltd
Old Station Drive
Leckhampton
CHELTENHAM   GL53 0DN
England

British Library Cataloguing in Publication Data

Teaching mathematics and art.
    1. Great Britain. Schools. Curriculum subjects:
    Mathematics. Teaching   2. Great Britain. Schools.
    Curriculum subjects: Visual arts. Teaching
    I. Jones, Lesley
    510.71041

ISBN 0-7487-0456-6

List of colour plates to be found between pp. 62–3:
Plate 4.1, Plate 4.2, Plate 4.3,
Plate 5.1, Plate 5.2, Plate 5.3, Plate 5.4, Plate 5.5,
Plate 7.1,
Plate 8.1, Plate 8.2, Plate 8.3.

Cover photograph reproduced by permission of the Trustees of the Wallace Collection.
Cover butterflies illustration © 1990 M. C. Escher Heirs/Cordon Art – Baarn – Holland.

Typeset by Tech-Set, Gateshead, Tyne & Wear.
Printed and bound in Great Britain at The Bath Press, Avon.

Contents

Preface

Many teachers already make links between art and mathematics in an informal way. I see evidence of this in schools: in mathematics and art which is displayed, and in journals which are aimed at practising teachers and contain contributions from them. Why then did I feel the need for this book? From talking to teachers I found that artwork which appeared to contain mathematics had not been considered in that light. Similarly, mathematics which could be used to develop an aspect of art had not been used in that way. The potential was there, but no capital had been made out of it. Art teachers were using mathematics with the children, but not making it explicit, while, for mathematics teachers, art often stopped at the level of display.

In most primary schools there is an interdisciplinary approach in which children explore a theme in many directions. With one teacher handling the whole curriculum this is not too difficult. However, the themes explored are often based in the humanities and developed to cover these disciplines together with language work and art. On the whole, mathematics is compartmentalised and not seen as a suitable area to tie in with such thematic work.

The situation in secondary schools has traditionally been rather different. Subjects are taught by specialists, generally in isolation from each other. Only recently has an impetus developed towards establishing cross-curricular links which allow children to explore themes which traverse the subject boundaries. Progress in this direction is very slow, not least because of the organisation of the timetable. Such institutionalised rigidity is very difficult to overcome and it takes a tremendous effort to bring about a change. There is also a tendency for cross-curricular links to be seen in a very instrumental way. The National Curriculum Council recommends that pupils 'meet and become secure with a particular mathematical idea or process at least one level earlier than they are required to use it in science.' (DES *Mathematics for Ages 5 to 16* 1988, §3.23) Thus mathematics is reduced to the level of handmaiden to science. The implication is that skills are learnt in mathematics and applied elsewhere. In fact, such fragmented teaching can lead to very limited understanding.

This book is intended to contribute in a practical way to a positive cross-curricular initiative. It provides a rationale for working across subject areas and suggests many practical ideas, firmly embedded in a theoretical background. It explores and explains the links between mathematics and art, providing practical suggestions which I hope will inspire the reader. These suggestions are backed up by a clear explanation of their educational basis. The fundamental ideas can be adapted to suit children of different abilities and age groups. The book starts from the premise that teachers are sensitive and resourceful people, ready to pounce on good ideas and supplement them with their own. The exercises provided within the book are intended to show how the ideas can be used, but they are not written directly for children. Teachers know the needs of the groups they teach and will need to modify and adapt the work to suit their pupils.

My hope is that teachers will use the book as a starting point for discussions with members of other departments in school and that themes will be developed in the context of these different departments. Such co-operation should help provide a more rounded curriculum for the pupils and help children to see the relevance of their work. The introduction of TVEE into all secondary schools has led to an increased emphasis on interdisciplinary approaches and an awareness that problems of the real world seldom fall into the compartments of subject disciplines. However, there is clearly a distinction between the kinds of judgements we make in mathematics and in art and this forms the focus of Nick McAdoo's discussion in the first chapter. It would seem that the most likely place to find cross-curricular work occurring in schools is at either end of the compulsory school age-range. Working with young children makes the interdisciplinary approach seem the natural way to work. When they are inspired and gripped by an idea, children do not concern themselves with its place in the curriculum. If it is extending and developing their thought processes it is unimportant whether it comes under the heading of 'mathematics' or 'art'. This holistic view is particularly obvious in the efforts of very young children to express themselves. The infant explores a surface through the medium of paint and develops artistic and mathematical concepts alongside each other. John Matthews provides a fascinating analysis of this in Chapter 2.

In Chapter 3 Keith Albarn traces the awareness of pattern, rhythm and proportion in the history of art and mathematics. The ideas discussed are wide-ranging and the themes introduced are developed further in other parts of the book. During my own art education at school, the only time I was explicitly aware of using mathematics was when I was introduced to perspective. In Chapter 4, William Wynne Willson explores the mathematics involved and describes the way in which it has been used in artistic works. Another aspect of geometry is considered by Jacky Plaster in Chapter 5. She looks at the work of some twentieth century painters and sculptors and discusses some of the interesting and surprising statements they have made about the ideas and processes they have used.

In Chapter 6 I indulged myself with a look at the work of M. C. Escher. His work has long been a matter of fascination for mathematicians and artists alike and I have worked with pupils who have been inspired and intrigued to develop their own ideas by following in his footsteps. Escher's tessellating patterns were themselves inspired by Islamic designs and it seems quite apt that Marilyn Metz focuses her attention on these. The work which she describes in Chapter 7 was really the stimulus which brought about the creation of this book. She and I had worked with students looking at the symmetry of Islamic patterns. It was an art book which finally provided the information which unlocked the door to these symmetries and brought us to an appreciation of just how much mathematics was intertwined with this particular branch of art.

It seems quite possible that the advance of microcomputers into schools may serve to break down barriers within the curriculum. John Bradshaw shows us in Chapter 8 how wonderful patterns have been hidden within mathematics. Using computer graphics we can release these images in a way which would be impossible without the power of the computer. Programs[1] can be used to help children who are hampered by their undeveloped motor skills from fully exploring some mathematical notions. With such instruments they can create glorious patterns and explore mathematics, giving full rein to their creative impulses.

In Chapter 9, Robert Dixon suggests a different approach to computer use in school, providing a sequential guide to programming computer graphics. Now that design is becoming a more familiar part of school work, there seems to be an opportunity in this area for mathematics and art teachers to work together for their mutual benefit.

It is perhaps inevitable that a book such as this will take a limited view of both mathematics and art, concentrating on aspects where the two have clear links. It will, however, be appreciated that this does not reflect a narrowness in the authors' perceptions of the subjects! Essentially the view of mathematics is biased towards the geometric aspects. Art is projected in a largely two-dimensional form, with considerable emphasis on pattern. I make no apology for this; pattern has a considerable contribution to make to art, especially in terms of folk culture, decorative art, textiles and so on. There are, unfortunately, large areas of interest which are omitted, including some which could provide further fertile starting points for mathematics/art links. The whole area of fabric design and textiles is perhaps the most obvious one.

LESLEY JONES

---

[1] Two good examples of such programs are 'Islam', Junior Maths, Earosoft and 'Tessellations', Cambridge University Press.

Acknowledgements

The authors and publishers are grateful to the following for permission to reproduce material:

The Trustees of The National Gallery, London for the photo on Plate 4.1;

Solomon R. Guggenheim Museum Collection, New York for the photo on Plate 4.2;

Glasgow Art Gallery and Museum for the photo on Plate 4.3;

Simon Penberthy for the photos on Plates 5.1, 5.2, 5.3, 5.4 and 5.5 and on pages 70–2;

Peter Tiller for the photo on Plate 7.1;

Vatican, Rome/Bridgeman Art Library, London for the photo on page 33;

Faber & Faber Ltd for the illustration on page 38 and the extracts from *The Modulor* by Le Corbusier on pages 37–8;

Macmillan Publishing Company for the illustration on page 39 and the extracts from *Synergetics* by R. Buckminster Fuller on pages 39–40;

The Ancient Art & Architecture Collection for the photos on pages 48–50;

Haags Gemeentemuseum for the photos on pages 51–2, 78 and 80;

M. C. Escher Heirs/Cordon Art for the photos on pages 51–2, 78 and 80 and the illustrations on pages 94–5;

The Trustees of the Wallace Collection for the photo on page 53;

The Syndics of the Fitzwilliam Museum, Cambridge for the photo on page 54;

Professor Dewdney for the quotations on pages 113 and 127;

Bill Richardson for the computer printout on page 124;

Jason Brown for the computer program on page 125;

National Museum of Scotland for the photo on page 137.

Every attempt has been made to contact copyright holders, but we apologise if any have been overlooked.

Contributors

Keith Albarn studied architecture and sculpture, ran an environmental design company in the sixties and formed the Vertex group in the seventies to research and design exhibitions including, in London, 'The World of Islam' and 'Illusion in Art, Nature and Science' and in Rotterdam, 'Islamathematica'. He is a co-author of *The Language of Pattern* and *Diagram* for Thames and Hudson, and has spent twenty years in art and design education. He is currently Head of the North Essex School of Art and Design at Colchester Institute.

John Bradshaw is Head of Mathematics at Torc High School in Tamworth. At the start of his initial training, he had difficulty in persuading his college to accept art as a complementary subject to mathematics. He has never regretted the combination. He is an active member of the Mathematical Association and an assistant editor of their journal *Mathematics in School*. The little time that is left is occupied with old cycles, motorcycles, cars and cameras. He is married to a primary school teacher and has two young children.

Robert Dixon graduated as a mathematician in the late sixties and spent four years at the Royal College of Art in the early eighties. He is currently teaching A-level mathematics while writing a practical book for beginners about computing the apparent position of the planets. He has frequently written on topics which combine art with mathematics for such periodicals as *New Scientist*, *Leonardo*, *Mathematics Teaching* and at greater length in his book *Mathographics*.

Lesley Jones taught in Birmingham primary and secondary schools for ten years, including a two-year secondment to the 'Progress Project' for gifted pupils. Since 1985 she has been a lecturer in education at Goldsmiths' College, London. Her particular interests are in developing cross-curricular links in schools and increasing the active and successful participation of girls in mathematics.

Nick McAdoo has degrees in English and philosophy from Cambridge and London and a PhD in Philosophy of Education. He taught for six years in inner-city primary schools in north London, including a three-year spell as Co-ordinator for English. From 1973 to 1977 he was Head of the Postgraduate Primary course at Rachel McMillan College and since 1977 he has been a lecturer in primary education at Goldsmiths' College, University of London. He has published many articles on aesthetic education.

John Matthews is an artist and art-educator who has had experience of teaching all age groups of children. His main area of research is concerned with the origin and development of representation in childhood. He has focused particular attention on the child's acquisition of drawing skills and their role in cognitive development. John has written papers, contributed to books and addressed international conferences about these concerns. He is at present a lecturer in the Faculty of Education, Goldsmiths' College, University of London.

Marilyn Metz is a lecturer at the Institute of Education, University of London. Prior to her involvement in higher education she taught five- to seven-year-olds in various London primary schools, being particularly interested in young children's use of LOGO. Her main concerns now lie in the fields of mathematics education and the role of computers across the curriculum.

Jacky Plaster taught for thirteen years, mostly in comprehensive schools in south-east London, before working as a lecturer in education at Goldsmiths' College, London. She is interested in art in relation to other curricular areas, such as mathematics, and also in feminist politics.

William Wynne Willson taught mathematics in secondary schools for 15 years before becoming a lecturer in mathematics education at Birmingham University. Both as a teacher and as an educationist he has had a particular interest in geometry; his book *The Mathematics Curriculum: Geometry* was published in 1977. Lately he has be concerned with the use of micros for geometry; he edited the Mathematical Association's *132 Short Programmes for the Mathematics Classroom.*

1 Mathematical and Aesthetic Perception: Some Philosophical Aspects

Nick McAdoo

Aesthetic form and representation of the world

It is hardly surprising that painters and mathematicians have often eyed each other's domains with interest. Insofar as the artist explores the inter-play of line, surface and volume within the 'space' of the canvas, all painting may be said to have a geometrical dimension which can be further divided into the two distinctive areas of aesthetic form and perspective. In the case of the latter, it is clear that the study of perspectival geometry has made a major contribution to solving the artist's problem of how to create the illusion of space on a flat surface, although it has also to be said that such a preoccupation with art as one-to-one correspondence has largely been confined to European art between the time of the Renaissance and the end of the nineteenth century. It is certainly not a necessary requirement of art that it must represent the world in a photographic manner, nor even that it must represent the world at all for that matter. This would be to de-legitimise any art such as Islamic, African or twentieth-century European abstract art, where representation of the world in the sense of photographic accuracy is of little importance.

The second way in which mathematics has made its presence felt is in its influence on that other, more universal goal of art, namely aesthetic form. By this, I mean any spatial configuration that fascinates and delights us for its own sake and not just for the subject matter that it represents or symbolises. From this point of view, the abstract perfection of geometrical shapes and ideal ratios has long held out to some artists the beguiling promise of a key that will unlock the secret of beauty. This may be seen in those works of art which explore such mathematically rich phenomena as the golden section, tessellation and the patterns generated by the Fibonacci sequence. The fascination of even very young infant artists with the balancing of symmetrical patterns may be seen in a quite dramatic way in the drawings by Oliver and William, aged three and a half (see Figures 1 and 2 on p. 2). Although, as we shall see in more detail later, the mathematical pursuit of symmetry can never be exactly identical with the drive of the artist to create harmonious form, there is a tradition of artistic recourse to such mathematical ideas that stretches from the ancient Greeks to twentieth-century abstract painters like Mondrian. This is, as often as not, associated with a cool classicism that seeks to counteract excessive romanticism in art with its over-emphasis on the subjectivity, and especially the emotional subjectivity, of the artist.

Figure 1 *Cathedral* by Oliver

Figure 2 *Me - swimming* by William

What then, of the mathematician's interest in art? It is clear that at least some of the pleasure that mathematicians take in their subject is of an aesthetic nature. By this, I mean that it involves a contemplative delight in the perception of form, such as when one is suddenly struck by the overall harmony of a collection of shapes over and above their individual mathematical or representational features, or when one sees a curving line not just as a 'curve' but as 'graceful', 'powerful' or 'dancing'. In this respect, young children who discover the delights of making patterns with their fingers in spilt blackcurrant puree are making discoveries not only of a proto-mathematical kind, but experiencing something not so very different from the pleasure that they may gain at a later age when a Cubist painting 'shapes up' for them into a miraculous crystalline structure of colour and form. Whether or not, at such an early age, they are also driven by an impulse to 'see pictures' in their fingermarks is a more debatable matter. The way that the circles one finds in infants' paintings soon start sprouting legs and arms and eventually faces may be, at least in part, a result of cultural conditioning which can, in fact, inhibit aesthetic development insofar as the young child comes to conceive of the primary function of art as accurate representation of the world. This may be seen when children, and many adults, first encounter abstract art forms. They invariably try to see in them something representational where nothing is intended, rather than simply enjoying the play of colour and form for its own sake. In the same way, when children are invited to make a collage out of coloured shapes, they will often turn their back on the rich possibilities for creating beautiful abstract configurations in favour of producing something crudely representational. Thus, a circle becomes a face and a triangle, a hat.

Following rules and feeling your way

There is of course, an undeniable pleasure to be found in representing the world, as may be seen when children play with the pictures that can be made from the Chinese tangram. However, without the additional ingredient of delight in form, it is a different kind of pleasure from that of the aesthetic. For a similar reason, aesthetic pleasure needs to be carefully separated from the pleasure that mathematicians, young and old, often take in producing perfectly symmetrical patterns – a pleasure that I would venture to suggest is more closely related to the human desire for order and regularity than aesthetic delight. Although artists are frequently concerned with the perception of balance and harmony, they have always subtly resisted the lure of perfect symmetry, even where they seem most to have pursued it. This can be seen in the patterns of Islamic textiles and ceramics. One reason for this is that a perfectly symmetrical pattern tends to be perceived, from an aesthetic point of view, as inert, whereas the introduction of an asymmetrical element, however seemingly marginal, may set the whole configuration into play. An example of this would be the way that the rotationally symmetrical outlines of the great rose windows which are found in many gothic cathedrals are rendered dynamic by the play of human figures and colours in the stained glass.

There is, however, an even more important reason for the need to separate the mathematician's pursuit of symmetry from the artist's pursuit of aesthetic form, which highlights perhaps the most fundamental difference of all between mathematical and aesthetic perception. Insofar as the concept of symmetry is, necessarily, totally rule-governed, symmetrical patterns can be produced quite mechanically. For example, a computer program is capable of generating endless proliferations of patterned squares divided symmetrically into halves, quarters, etc. In order to identify aesthetic pleasure with such configurations one would be forced into saying that the results were automatically beautiful. However, this would be to go against one of the most deep-rooted of all aesthetic beliefs, namely, that the creation of aesthetically pleasing forms, like our appreciation of them, contains a necessary element of *spontaneity* that, by definition, must escape the net of any sufficient set of rules. The very notion of aesthetic creativity, for all that it is constrained by cultural conventions, implies a kind of 'leap into the dark' such as the twentieth-century painter, Paul Klee describes when he talks of 'taking a line for a walk' which *may* follow a regular pattern, but which, at every point, is free to wander off into the uncharted territory of aesthetic creation which no quantifiable rule can predict. The German philosopher Kant expresses a similar notion with regard to the necessarily spontaneous element that lies at the heart of aesthetic appreciation, when he argues that:

> There can be no rule according to which anyone is to be forced to recognise anything as beautiful.
>
> Kant, 1965

3

Of course, once the work has been produced, one may attempt a mathematical analysis of its spatial properties by, perhaps, taking a graceful line in a particular painting and plotting its course mathematically. However, this could not yield a general rule for the production of graceful lines, but only a rule for producing carbon copies of *that* particular line, whereas every graceful line in art is graceful after its own fashion (Scruton, 1974, p. 33).

In the absence of any ready-to-hand rules for the creation or appreciation of art, it is widely held that one develops a feeling for what is aesthetically satisfying. The problem with this, however, is that by contrast with the objectivity and precision of mathematical judgment, such a feeling would appear, at first glance, to be hopelessly subjective and therefore ineducable. This is embodied in the familiar subjectivist slogan that 'beauty is in the eye of the beholder'. If this were indeed the case, then one of its consequences would be a totally fragmented view of the relationship between mathematics and art, rendering any *aesthetic* enjoyment of mathematical form as arbitrary as, for example, seeing pictures in the cracks in the plaster.

The main question which needs to be addressed therefore, is this: what, if anything, *is* the relationship between the objectively measurable properties of spatial configurations and the seemingly far more personal aesthetic impression that they make on the viewer? To put the problem more concretely, what is the relationship between, for example, seeing a line as curved and seeing the *same* line as graceful?

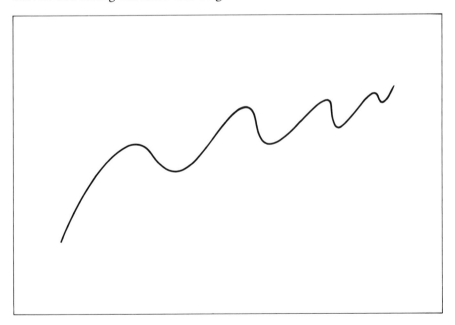

Figure 3

Aestheticians such as Frank Sibley and Ruby Meager have made an interesting attempt both to clarify this relationship and, at the same time, to avoid the 'anything goes' impasse of extreme subjectivism, by drawing an important distinction between what have come to be called the *primary* and the *emergent* features of works of art. The concept of a primary feature is used to denote all those obvious, measurable, everyday features of the work that anyone with normal powers of perception and intelligence can discern – for example, that the line in Figure 3 is an undulating curve, or that a painting by Picasso shows an old man playing the guitar, the whole composition being painted in various shades of blue and measuring 100 cm by 80 cm. Our ability to perceive such primary features is, for the most part, fairly uncontentious. However, where controversy does arise, it is usually settled without too much difficulty by appealing to objective and clear-cut criteria. For example, in the unlikely event of a pupil refusing to see that the line is curved, the matter is quickly settled by explaining that *any* line is curved if its direction continuously deviates from a straight line. Again, in the case of the Picasso painting, we might notice on closer inspection that the instrument on which the old man is playing is a mandolin and not a guitar. It is a further feature of such perception that our feelings are not especially engaged and that furthermore, we can get a fairly clear picture of the object from an accurate second-hand description, without having seen it 'in the flesh'.

By contrast, the concept of an emergent feature is used to denote the way in which the primary object may sometimes 'shape up' into an emotionally charged whole or gestalt which is somehow more than the sum of its primary components. There is nothing particularly mysterious about this, for a range of such perceptions are commonly to be found in everyday life: a building seems to be friendly or oppressive, or a landscape takes on a cheerful aspect. It is towards this type of configuration, a configuration that emerges from the primary features of our perceptual field, that aesthetic perception is directed. It is recognisable by the special kind of delight that we find ourselves taking in such an aspect. Thus, while one gazes at the curved line, it may seem to flow and dance with infinite grace, like a wave continuously breaking and re-forming. In the same way, while gazing at the Picasso painting mentioned previously, it may strike us as bathed in an atmosphere of intense sadness that emerges out of the interplay of blue on blue.

The main problem, for the teacher as for the pupil, is that such emergent aspects do not yield themselves in the same clear-cut way as do primary features. There is no definitive 'book of rules' to which we can appeal (as we can in the case of our perception of the primary features) in order to justify the emergent aspect that we find ourselves experiencing. Thus, while everyone with normal eyesight and intelligence can come to see that the line is curved, not everyone will be able, so automatically, to see the gracefulness in the line, nor is there any way of compelling them to see it if they cannot. This is because, in the absence of any sufficient set of criteria for such aesthetic concepts as gracefulness, their legitimate application ultimately comes to rest in a highly personal experience which is very much dependent upon the imaginative and emotional susceptibility of the individual. Furthermore, insofar as the feelings are necessarily engaged, there is an unavoidable involuntary element in aesthetic perception over which we can never have full control. We may know at an educated level, for example, that when we gaze at a Cubist still-life, it ought to strike us as a wonderful harmony of crystalline shapes, waking us up to the splendours of the everyday perceptual world that we have come to take too much for granted. Yet the harder we gaze at it, the more it appears to us as nothing more than a very distorted blue guitar surrounded by a jumble of unrelated coloured patches! We could, of course, learn, as some pupils do, to fake a response by 'saying all the right things', much as one pretends to laugh at a joke that one does not understand, but this would be a grotesque parody of aesthetic education.

However, while art teachers need always to encourage pupils to report their personal responses, or lack of them, honestly, at the same time they must equally encourage an openness to new aesthetic experiences. Otherwise, the pupils will remain trapped within the ghetto of their own tastes. From this point of view, it is always the aim of the art teacher to take the children beyond the obvious, primary features of the work towards a perception of its emergent features wherein the work of art comes alive aesthetically. If the pupils' perception remains stuck at the primary level, then it is hardly surprising that they come to see art as a fairly pointless activity, for, seen thus, what *is* the point of representing the world on canvas when you can go out and see the real thing for yourself? At best, art will come to be seen as a second-hand version of real life: a landscape painting provides us with a convenient substitute for a good view out of the sitting room window. Furthermore, from this point of view, all abstract art will come to be seen as particularly pointless and absurd.

How then, is it possible not only to justify the claims of aesthetic perception but to communicate them to others? Justification and communication are always closely linked, as they are in any area of human understanding. It can hardly be doubted that there must be some relationship of dependency between the rule-governed and measurable primary features of the work and the aesthetic gestalt or form which emerges from these features. If we were to rub out the curve, the gracefulness would clearly not remain hovering invisibly in the air. We do, as matter of fact, quite often appeal to primary aspects of the work when we attempt to justify our experience of its emergent aesthetic aspects. To take a fairly simple example, I may say that I find the curve in Figure 3 graceful because of the way that its undulations are repeated on a diminishing scale. Now this can never constitute a conclusive proof in the way that I can conclusively prove that it is a curve, yet it is not as arbitrary as the chance associations that may lead me to see pictures in the cracks in the plaster. There may be many legitimate ways in which I may perceive the curved line aesthetically, for example, as flowing or dancing, but there are limits as to what might count as an appropriate response. I doubt if anyone, for instance, unless there were very special reasons, could see it as violent or threatening.

It is this looser concept of appropriateness rather than hard-line objectivity that distinguishes aesthetic arguments from mathematical ones while, at the same time, allowing a modest degree of rationality and therefore, educability, to enter into aesthetic discussion. Thus, while I can never force anyone to see the gracefulness in the curved line, I may, through appealing to other people's sense of appropriateness, get them to see it for themselves. Insofar as the legitimacy of my aesthetic judgment depends, in the end, on reaching at least a modicum of agreement with others, I may well find that, after discussion, some of my aesthetic perceptions come to strike me as inappropriate, and that I now see the work in a different light. For example, someone else, by pointing out some primary feature of the curve that I had not noticed, may come to convince me that, far from being graceful, it is powerful or bursting with energy. However, one should not necessarily feel defeated if an aesthetic disagreement remains unresolved, for it may well be in the nature of any aesthetic configuration that a variety of equally appropriate responses are possible. Nevertheless, this is not at all the same thing as accepting the extreme subjectivist viewpoint that 'anything goes', which would be to make the concept of aesthetic education a contradiction in terms. We cannot hope for more than this without destroying that element of spontaneity that lies at the heart of all aesthetic perception.

Given then, that the central problem of relating mathematics to art is that of establishing a relationship between the rule-governed primary world of the former and the more personal, less predictable emergent world of the latter, how are teachers to communicate to pupils (or pupils to teachers for that matter), such elusive phenomena as the gracefulness in a curved line? As with most teaching, there is no single way (Sibley, 1962, pp. 81–3). Sometimes an analogy will help, like comparing the line to the motion of a wave, or the wind rippling through the long grass. At other times, the teacher may need to alert the pupils to certain primary features that they may have missed, such as the special way in which the shape of the curve repeats itself. The primary and emergent features may be placed side by side, as when the primary combination of mathematical intricacy and regularity is related to the feeling of delicacy intimated by the curve's gracefulness. Discussion with pupils may also focus on their own experiences of graceful movement, such as skating. At other times, one may simply invite them to see the gracefulness in the curve, perhaps by using a certain tone of voice, and that will convey the message. Alternatively, a gesture such as a flowing movement of the hand may sometimes succeed where words fail.

The common ground

In the end, however, pupils either see it or they don't. Yet is the situation really so very different within the field of mathematics, for example when, despite all the teacher's careful guidance, a pupil still fails to see the key that will unlock the secret of a number progression? In this respect, mathematical perception may have more in common with aesthetic perception than might at first appear. There is a sense in which the over-simplistic identification of mathematics with reason, and the Arts with feeling is as much a caricature of mathematics as it is of the Arts. This is because, just as aesthetic discourse is inseparable from the rational demand that it be in some way appropriate to its object, so equally, the discourse of mathematics comes to rest in a feeling for the self-evidence of its most basic axioms. Such a feeling cannot itself be justified mathematically for the simple reason that one cannot use mathematical argument to justify mathematical argument without getting very quickly into an infinite regress. Thus, any mathematical system has to presuppose a given foundation, such as the self-evident laws of identity and non-contradiction, that cannot itself be justified from within the system because the system, at every point, presupposes it. It is therefore, only upon the condition that children possess such a feeling that mathematical understanding can get off the ground.

Finally, there is yet another reason why the aesthetic realm may not be so very different from the mathematical one. Although, as we have seen, aesthetic perception can never be rule-governed in the same way as mathematics, it is clearly governed by rules of a sort, in the sense that, however open-ended our conceptions of art, not just anything can be a 'painting' or a 'drawing'. Otherwise, such terms would be meaningless. In all cultures, the Arts are subject to conventions, traditions and styles which may be followed or rebelled against but which cannot be ignored on pain of unintelligibility. Admittedly, the conventions that govern Renaissance art, Cubism or African masks do not have the same degree of certainty as the rules which govern mathematical equations. This is why they can be challenged and modified, even in an extreme way, as the European Dada movement challenged the whole Western conception of art after the First World War. Nonetheless, one could not even make sense of Dada without first grasping something of the traditions against which it was so strongly protesting. For example, in a Dada exhibition shortly after the war, Marcel Duchamp displayed a picture postcard of the Mona Lisa with half her teeth blacked out and wearing a curly black moustache! Furthermore, even in the very act of breaking all the rules, a new set of rules must inevitably start to emerge – in this case, the rules of Dada. The meaning of 'Dada', like the meaning of any word, is inseparable from the notion of a rule however elusive that rule may be. It would seem then, that there is no more an unbridgeable divide between mathematical and aesthetic perceptions than there is between primary and emergent perception in general. From this the conclusion that teachers of mathematics and teachers of art have much to learn from each other will come as no surprise. This, in turn, can only lead to a richer and more holistic education for their pupils.

CHAPTER **2** # How Children Map 3D Volumes and Scenes on to 2D Surfaces

John Matthews

Introduction

The purpose of this chapter is to illuminate for teachers some of the mathematical understandings implicit in children's drawings. Lesley Jones has pointed out in the preface to this book, that teachers do not always realise the mathematical thinking to be found in their pupils' art work. Art teachers themselves have not always been clear about the contribution drawing makes to cognitive development. Perhaps, for these reasons, art has traditionally been squeezed to the periphery of the school curriculum, yet it plays an important role in children's development and thinking.

Having said this, it is important to state, right from the outset, that the intention here is not to make yet another apology for art education, of the kind which degrades art into a mere servicing tool for other subjects. Rather, the intention is to show that, essential to the nature of art itself, and to the moves children make in the acquisition of drawing skills, is a family of mathematical understandings. The concern in this chapter is for one subset of this family: the spatial and geometric aspects.

All the mathematical understandings implicit in art are, to be sure, suffused with expressive and emotional values. Nick McAdoo pointed out in the previous chapter that lines, shapes and marks cannot be described solely in mathematical terms. However, since it is not generally appreciated that mathematics is embedded within art, it does seem worthwhile to explicate and highlight these aspects. In doing so, we may not only deepen our understanding of mathematics but also heighten our perception of art. It is further hoped that this chapter will point the way toward teaching principles which might best support and encourage creative thinking within these disciplines.

Children use drawing, amongst other forms of representation, as a means of forming descriptions of the world. Even the drawings of very young children encode some important perceptions they are developing about the causal relations within events, perceptions about what makes objects move and what makes people move, as well as perceptions about the relations between and within objects (Wolf and Fucigna, 1983; Smith, 1983; Matthews, 1984, 1988, 1989, 1990).

9

From its very beginnings, drawing contributes to and reflects the child's spatial and mathematical understanding. As children grow up, so their drawing reflects the different kinds of knowledge which they are developing. Children attend to those spatial relations they consider the most powerful and significant; the significance they attach to certain relations changes with age. Initially, the child (between two and five years) attends to stable topological relations including inside/outside, hollowness, boundary, proximity and continuity. In later childhood and adolescence however, their drawings are transformed by changes in the priorities about the kind of spatial/geometrical information they consider essential in a drawing. In particular, they feel the need to map projective relations on to the drawing surface. In translating 3D solids and scenes into 2D, children develop some unexpected geometrical systems (Willats, 1981, pp. 18–33 and 1985, pp. 78–100).

Unfortunately, such systems are not always understood by adults and, as a consequence, children do not always receive appropriate teaching. Yet such drawing systems do reflect powerful mathematical thinking, in which the essential structure of objects and events is mapped on to the drawing surface. It is both tragic and ironic that the development of such graphic descriptions is mostly stunted in children in our society, for such systems – in their developed form – are employed by artists, designers and scientists the world over. They are used as tools to resolve spatio-mathematical problems and as a means of visualising complex structure. This is as true of the beginnings of drawing as it is of drawing produced in later childhood and adolescence. At all levels, it should be stressed, drawing not only reflects the child's perceptions, it also initiates and guides the child's investigation of forms, relations and structures in the world.

Although the main emphasis of this book is on later childhood and adolescence, my own experience in education has taught me that it is easier to understand drawing at this level if one knows something of the background of the development of drawing in early infancy. Drawing, during teenage life, forms part of a continuum of symbolisation whose onset can be traced back to birth.

Early mark-making

In early infancy, from six months to three years, children experiment with mark-making as part of a holistic and systematic search of the structural and expressive potential of their own bodies and the environment. They begin to perceive the relationships between their own actions and the effects of these on objects. They become conscious that different actions have different effects, and learn how to initiate these actions, and how to repeat them, in order to obtain the effects. In the beginnings of drawing, space is defined by action (Piaget and Inhelder 1956; Brookes, 1974). This functionally dependent relationship is a mathematical principle which has enormous implications for drawing. There are other levels too, in which the relationships between actions and images are of deep and lasting significance. By performing actions upon the world, children develop representations of their own bodies, and their own body actions. In a mutually reciprocal relationship with this process, is the development of representations of objects upon which actions are performed. These internal representations or models involve mathematical descriptions. Without the formation of internal models, the use of symbolic systems – including mathematics – is just not possible.

Drawing plays a key role in the formation of these internal models. From sensorimotor actions which leave traces or records of their passing, infants (from six months to four years) begin to attribute expressive values to their mark-making actions and to the resultant effects. This is not only an investigation of the pragmatic and instrumental possibilities of their actions – the children also exploit their own actions for their *expressive* potential. As I have stated elsewhere (Matthews, 1984, pp. 1–39 and 1988, pp. 162–83) far from being haphazard and meaningless scribbling, mark-making media, in the hands of even a two-year-old, can be an expressive vehicle capable of reflecting the most subtle changes and nuances in the emotional temperature of the interpersonal environment. Graphic tracings, resulting from natural movements of multi-articulated limbs define basic vectors or axes of the body. The first drawing, then, takes place within a self-referential coordinate frame or envelope of personal body-space. It is at this level that the child organises into co-ordinated sequences of movements, a repertoire of mark-making actions. Early drawing behaviour is an orchestrated, rhythmical pattern of events. Drawing actions are often synchronised by vocalisations or movements of other parts of the body, which serve to underscore qualities emerging in the actions and marks. It is from such instinctive rhythmical patterning, that the child begins to form a sense of the equivalence between different actions – that is, actions which issue from distinctly different sensorimotor systems. The child of two years might, for example, associate the stamping and beating of the feet to the stabbing impacts of a paint-laden brush. The child might go on to synchronise, in one-to-one correspondence, onomatopoeic vocalisations to such impacts of the brush (Matthews, 1990, 1990a).

This is the beginning of *counting*. The child is counting his or her own actions. He or she is associating an arbitrary tag, or *numeron* (Gelman and Gallistel, 1983, p. 191) to actions and resultant marks. The complexity of the internal action programmes required to produce counting behaviour – starting and stopping at the right time, speaking and pointing (or marking) in synchrony, pointing accurately at the unit to be counted (and not at the spaces in-between) has been remarked upon by Gelman and Gallistel (1983). Two-year-olds are very interested in counting. Early drawing and painting can aid this experience.

Counting does not seem to be copied from the behaviour of older children or adults, but is initiated and driven by deep structures which may be represented in the central nervous system. This is an important point and one which is also true for the acquisition of symbol systems generally. Imitation from surrounding cultural exemplars does not appear to be the main mechanism for development (Willats, 1977, 1981, 1985). The idea that development is largely self-driven and regulated by internal aims, standards and attainment targets is a cause of surprise and even disbelief for some, but it is an important feature of development and one which clearly spells out a special approach to educational provision.

The child also associates vocalisations to mark-making events in other ways. One might see melodic vocalisations mapped on to the production of lines which are trailed across the paper. Ascending vocalisations are synchronised to the production of lines describing inverted arcs. Such events often carry symbolic play scenarios in which imagined objects describe rising and falling flight. The child attends to the beginnings and ends of these trajectories: slowing down, speeding up or re-running sequences. Sometimes the child synchronises to the moment of the line's termination, explosive vocalisations designed to emphasise an imagined moment of impact. Occasionally, these termini are demarcated by dots, slashes or other marks; line-endings are even ringed by rotational movements.

These *continuous rotations* are of great significance in drawing development, and have important mathematical meanings associated with them. Early energetic to-ing, fro-ing, pushing and pulling of the marker is synthesised into a continuous rotation. These dynamic elliptical movements, with their residue in pigment traces of overlaid spirals, acquire powerful expressive values of several kinds. One such is the *action representation* (Matthews, 1984, 1988, 1990). This occurs within the ongoing act of drawing itself and can specify complex events, for example, the flight of an aeroplane or the action of washing one's hands. Alternatively, the resultant trace can be considered by the child as an image conveying *configurative* values. This means that the elliptical or circular mark specifies to the child a discernable unit in space.

This latter possibility becomes clearer as the child learns to produce the *closed shape*. For many infants this shape is derived from the continuous rotation, though its detection and use really signifies a great conceptual leap made by the child. This form is of great mathematical significance. It is sometimes referred to by a mathematical term – a *Jordan's curve*. With this shape, the child has a range of mathematical options. In the placing of spots, squiggles or blobs and, later on, more complex configurations within or without the perimeter line of the closed shape, the child can specify *inside/outside* relationships.

As the child generates this form, so his or her attention is increasingly turned to any new manifestation of this relationship within the environment. This is encoded on to the drawing surface by the use of closed shapes and nuclei.

The closed shape can also represent an object in the world as a generalised unitary whole. The topological character of children's early drawing has been noted by Piaget and Inhelder (1956). They are developing a system of representation which captures and preserves some of the features and relations of objects – enclosure, boundary, hollowness, continuity – whilst neglecting others, namely, angles, proportions, viewpoints and depth relations. However, it would be wrong to consider this system in terms of deficits. It is a system which is employed precisely because it captures those very features and properties of the world which have especial salience at this phase of the child's development.

There are, in any case, other reasons why one should be cautious in considering the child at this level as engaged in a solely topological description of the world. At the same time as using the closed shape to convey generalised holistic volumes, he or she also uses it to denote the faces of objects, in drawings which specify the viewer's relation to the scene. Elsewhere (Matthews, 1989, pp. 127–41) I have described how even a three-year-old may use a line to specify a plane seen along a line-of-sight at zero degrees, that is, totally foreshortened, and closed shapes which represent planes orientated (at least notionally) at 90 degrees to the viewer's line-of-sight. Hence, even the very young child shows dawning projective understandings, an ability, incidently, not predicted by Piaget.

Whichever the closed shape is used to represent (volume, face or section) the perimeter line in each case starts to take on some remarkable characteristics. Where the closed shape stands for the generalised form of an object, the line denotes a holistic boundary, in the sense of the interface between one medium and another. This is true of the line as a section, though in a rather different sense. Here, the line represents an interface which can only be imagined. My own research shows that very young children are capable of making this conceptual leap.

The child also groups actions and marks into sets or families. Sometimes marks of a particular character are grouped in special sub-divisions of a closed shape. This is an example of early mathematical *logic* or *set theory*.

Other classification procedures are adopted. Notionally parallel, notionally vertical lines are grouped together. Sometimes they are assembled so that their lengths are matched (Smith, 1983). The *beginnings* and *ends* of lines are noted as significant. These are also clearly indicated on the drawing surface. These procedures are robust. They constitute deep structures which the child discerns across a range of superficially different contexts (Athey, 1980, pp. 4–9; Matthews, 1984, 1988). For example, when drawing nuclei inside closed shapes, the child may display the same conceptual concern as when he/she deposits toys or other objects inside various containers. The child investigates – with both striking systematism and enthusiasm – a whole range of situations in which one object can be subsumed with the volume of another. In doing so, the child builds up, not only knowledge of inside and outside relationships, but also constructs representations of the form of objects, including their relative sizes, plus the relationships between features of an individual object.

Though much misunderstood, maligned and mistreated, such, in fact, is the power of early so-called 'scribbling'.

Later development

With this background it is now possible to describe the drawing of later childhood and adolescence. The graphic schemes developed by the young child have initiated and guided perception of forms within the environment. With these schemes, or programmes of search, the child has built internal models or descriptions which have a geometric and logico-mathematical basis.

The experiences young children have with physical objects in the world – objects which can be handled or climbed upon, pushed or rolled, thrown or broken, with volumes through which one can crawl, with real spaces through which one can project one's body or voice, or through which one can run, jump, swing or fall – have been reflected in their drawing systems. The functions of these systems have included alerting the child to any new manifestation or variation in the deep structures which underlie these experiences.

We have seen that the child forms *equivalences* in drawing and painting in many senses. Some of these equivalences are *dynamic*, in that events in the world are being represented by events occuring on a two-dimensional surface. Other equivalences are *configurative*, that is, a drawn shape or combination of shapes can be said to stand for an entity in the world. This latter kind of equivalence works because configuration abstracts and preserves one element of the physical entity to which it refers, namely, its *shape*.

Children make a further kind of equivalence of a different class when they make a one-to-one correspondence between action and mark. This is an equivalence in the rather special sense that a mark is the *same* as a sound, or another action. One can say that a pictorial symbol *stands for*, say, a person, a dog, or a house, but we tend to say that 100 pence is the *same* as £1, or, more simply, 100 pence is a pound. This kind of equivalence formed between events occurring on the 2D surface, and other events, plays a fundamental part in assisting the child to form mathematical models of the world.

However, the child has to move to quite new systems of equivalences when it comes to the encoding of a new kind of information he or she is gathering from the environment. With a limited vocabulary the child is now in a position to specify generalised, unitary bound volumes, sometimes with attached lines which specify connected tubular volumes. The child can also specify certain relationships between and within forms, such as inside/outside, and has moved on to making further stipulations about exactly where forms are situated within a closed shape. Dots or spots enclosed within the closed shape can specify forms, such as eyes which are (to use John Willats' 1985 terms) not saliently extended in any dimension.

The child has made the discovery that the placing of configurations in positions along a longitudinal axis of the paper can specify higher/lower relations in the real world. Bigger and smaller relations can also be encoded in two dimensions. The child can show dynamic trajectories of objects in space, and also, in the placing of marks with a pair of parallel grouped lines, the child can show the passage made by an object through a hollow, tubular form.

How is it possible, though, to show 'going through' in quite a different sense – that of passing back through the picture plane itself? In other words, how is it possible to represent depth relations on a flat surface? How can you show that one object is behind another object? How is it possible to map the third dimension on to the drawing surface?

My own observations show that, first of all, in attempting to show the passage back through the picture plane, the child may resort to physically piercing holes through the surface of the paper itself! Joel, aged two years and eleven months, after describing, with the tracing of a felt-tip pen, the movements of climbers around and around, and then up and down a mountain, proceeded to push the pen through the paper to show the people climbing through the mountain (Matthews, 1984, 1989, 1990). Hannah, aged three years and five months, punched a hole through her drawing of 'dancers', pushed a small toy figure through the hole and then remarked: 'I danced through the hole and fell through . . . It [the paper] has a hole in the other side – it has to have!' [She laughs].

As the child attempts to show, in 2D, more of the truth about the world, so some other extraordinary drawings are produced. The information acquired by moving around the environment uniquely specifies classes of objects and children organise systems of representation from which they can recover this essential structure.

In trying to convey the structures and relations within and between objects, their different features and faces – which could not possibly be seen from a single viewpoint – are sometimes opened up or folded-out. In such drawings one obtains a multiplicity of views or aspects of the object or scene, simultaneously. These drawings have in fact been termed 'fold-out' drawings. In, for example, a drawing of a cuboid, children will explode its form to show that it does indeed have six faces. Because they look so strange, such drawings are frequently misunderstood and demeaned, and consequently, children become ashamed of them. They in fact require praise and encouragement, for they have discovered how to make *object-centred* depictions (Marr, 1982; Willats, 1985). This is a powerful system capable of preserving the main structure and axes of objects, irrespective of the arbitrary viewpoint.

Children do go on to develop a drawing system capable of encoding an axis back through the picture-plane. This system uses vertical and horizontal lines and is called *vertical oblique* (Willats, 1977, 1981, 1985). In this system, side-to-side in the picture stands for side-to-side in the real world, up-and-down in the picture stands for up-and-down in the real world, but the vertical axis is used to specify the third dimension also. It is a remarkable discovery made by the child. Its appearance supports the idea that drawing development is essentially creative and is not determined by, or limited to, the availability of

15

cultural examples. Children are unlikely to have seen pictures constructed from the vertical oblique system – though, interestingly enough, some Persian and Indian pictures use this system (as stated by John Willats in a personal letter, 1989). He has claimed that children might discover the vertical oblique projection by learning to stop at the right moment during their 'fold-out' drawings and so leave a possible view of the object. It may be, however, that the child alternates between different systems depending on the context.

As John Willats has pointed out, one problem with the vertical oblique system is the potential ambiguity in that the vertical axis stands simultaneously for two directions in the real world. One way out of this difficulty is to use lines with a third orientation – the *oblique* line.

Children's difficulties in representing an axis back through the picture-plane have often been attributed to motor problems in producing the necessary lines and line junctions. For example, it is often thought that very young children initially lack the skills to produce the oblique lines required within certain projective drawing systems. In fact, observations of natural drawing development and experimental work (Phillips, Hobbs and Pratt, 1978, pp. 15–33) show this to be untrue. The apparent failure to encode the third dimension cannot be accounted for solely in terms of motor difficulties.

The child already has in his or her possession those very structures necessary to convey depth on to the drawing surface. What is required is actually a new psychological orientation to those very schemata already available to the child. When trying to draw volumetric solids, the child brings to these new drawing tasks, knowledge acquired from his or her prior experience. As useful as his or her programmes of search have been up to now, they require radical adjustments when it comes to encoding further specifications about his or her experiences in the world.

Schemata are instructions about what to see, and what to do with what you see. They are generalisations about actions and objects without which we cannot live. However, these generalisations are periodically challenged by sudden new insights. This is precisely what happens when children move toward projective systems of drawing.

One important feature of rectangular, carpentered objects is that top and bottom surfaces are horizontal, and sides are vertical. The inclined plane is a dynamic vector for the child. Objects roll down slopes; towers cannot be built upon them. On large slopes one can tumble and fall and hurt oneself.

The child has found that the oblique line has been perfectly adequate for representing a slope. However, this symbolic value comes into conflict with a new order of information. For example, in some kinds of projective systems, an oblique line can be used to denote, not a slope, but an axis back through the picture-plane itself. In a depiction of rectangular or cuboidal objects, it is a momentous achievement when the child realises that the sloping line does not necessarily have to mean a slope. This enormous discovery is that an *oblique* line can represent a *horizontal* line, but one which recedes back through the picture-plane.

From this time, the picture-plane itself comes to be regarded, not just as a physical target at which to aim the marker, but as a transparent, vertically aligned cross-section of space itself: a window which opens out on to a sample of the optical array. The child's use of the oblique line as an *orthogonal* line signals a leap from one symbolic system to another.

With the depiction of curved, smooth forms, like the human figure, the child is also required to denote kinds of edges which are very different from those which are present in faceted objects. In these latter objects, edges can be physically touched. In smooth, curved forms, however, edges exist only in the sense of *occluding boundaries*. Their existence is a function of a particular, fixed viewpoint, and their character changes as the viewer moves.

In developing drawing systems which specify three-dimensional objects and arrays, the child is required to generate an increasingly complex set of drawing rules (Willats, 1981, 1985). This means that development in children's drawings is related to the changing values they attribute to shapes, lines, line orientations and the junctions of lines.

The discovery of perspective also creates further challenges to the child's descriptions of reality so far. Consider, for example, the child's understanding of parallel lines. The child's experience of carpentered objects – including perhaps, play with building blocks, or Lego® – has taught the child the importance of *congruence* between parallel edges. Unless this relation is preserved, towers topple. Similarly, the appreciation that parallel lines run in the same direction is essential information if you are trying to get the wheels of your toy car on the road, the wheels of your toy train on the track, or if you are trying to align accurately and efficiently your toy chairs around the table in the dolls' house.

Because of these experiences, parallel lines and parallel groupings take on deep significance to the child, a significance which is reflected in children's drawings at various times in their lives. Such experiences of rigid, Euclidean geometry have important practical applications for the child. However, as the child matures, his or her attention is increasingly attuned to depth relations in both the real world, and in drawings. He or she encounters carpentered or rectangular objects in which the parallel edges actually *converge* to a vanishing point at optical infinity. This is the *perspective* system.

It is at this point that we may see in children's drawing, further competition or conflict between two or more sorts of knowledge. The earlier knowledge derives from *object-centred* descriptions which preserve the natural and enduring features and relations within forms irrespective of viewpoint which, for example, tells the child that parallel edges remain parallel. The new kind of knowledge is concerned with the appearance of an object from a fixed viewpoint in space. Descriptions which capture this kind of information have been termed *viewer-centred* (Marr, 1982). A group of projective drawing

17

systems capture this kind of information, but perspective most unambiguously specifies the viewer's own relation to the scene.

As the child begins to appreciate that pictures can convey depth information, he or she still brings to these new experiences, those structural principles which have served him or her so well in the past, in that they preserved features of reality considered essential. The child tries to show this new depth information in drawings but at the same time does not wish to sacrifice what he or she knows is the truth about objects. Certain relations remain invariant despite other transformations the objects undergo, and despite movements the child might make around and between the objects. Also, objects do not physically shrink as they recede into the distance. However, in order to convey projective relations on the drawing surface, it is this very information which has to be constrained. In drawing projective relations, it is necessary to override the knowledge which, in everyday experience, enables us to operate in a world of real objects and events.

During this transitional phase then, the child might achieve a synthesis between these different types of information. New, viewer-centred information that parallel lines *appear* to converge at infinity is sometimes combined with object-centred information which tells the child that in no way, for example, can the floor and ceiling of a railway carriage ever touch! Other object-centred information may further complicate matters by informing the child that railway carriages can be entered from two sides. In my own observation, object-centred and viewer-centred information was combined in exactly this way in a child's drawing of a railway train coming straight toward the viewer. This is shown in Figure 1. Oblique parallel lines were used to convey receding horizontal edges of the carriages yet still two sides of the carriage were shown simultaneously, plus a plan aspect of the railway track (Matthews, 1989).

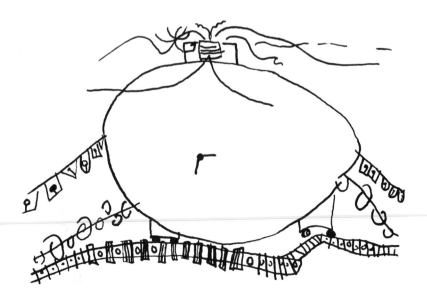

Figure 1

18

This child had been collecting perspective pictures of railway trains and photographs which are automatically in perspective. Yet, though these dramatic pictures were obviously intriguing to the child, in his own drawings, the perspectival convergence of parallel lines was initially rejected in favour of a system which preserved both parallelism and the multi-faceted nature of the object.

Conclusion

The degree to which a child is able to assimilate forms from the surrounding pictorial environment is directed and influenced by those very schemata of representation he or she is generating. This is a feature of development of extreme importance in education. Our input to children should be carefully matched to their developing programmes of enquiry. These are like dynamic templates through which experiences are filtered. An exact congruence between provision and these dynamic templates, even if this were possible, is neither necessary or desirable. In fact, for development to occur, existing schemata have to be challenged by experiences which do not quite fit them.

For drawing development to be supported, teachers need to be able to identify the approaches to representation through which children move as they grow. What happens so often is that children, due to lack of understanding and support, find it painful to continue with the struggle to iron out the ambiguities they perceive in their drawings.

Whilst it is sometimes claimed that drawing development is a solitary process my own evidence shows quite clearly that drawing, like other symbolic systems, is highly sensitive to the interpersonal context. Children are better able to make the shifts in the type and range of their representational systems if they have the encouragement and support of adults. As children try to capture more of the essential structure and relations of objects, so they produce drawings which may appear very strange to some adults. These drawings are not to be judged incorrect efforts which could be improved if only children could be made to somehow 'look harder' at nature. It is sometimes glibly stated that if children were able to draw in perspective then they would simply do so. Whilst they may say that they want to make their pictures 'more realistic', the precise nature of this desire is very complex. They will resist a system if it distorts information they feel essential.

The foregoing description of development is not to be taken to mean that there exists a hierarchical series of drawing systems, with earlier, inferior ones replaced by later, superior ones and perspective as the ultimate in representational geometry. This is a peculiarly western ethnocentric notion. The systems the children move through recall those perfectly legitimate systems used in exquisite drawings and paintings produced at various times

19

and in various places in the world. It is sad that, whilst encouraging children to value the art of different cultures, the self-same systems which these employ – when they appear in children's drawings – are viewed so negatively. Unfortunately, this failure to identify representational systems when they appear in either a Persian miniature or in a child's drawing, reflects badly on education generally and on some aspects of anti-racist education.

The planning of appropriate education provision and interaction for drawing development requires that adults identify the symbolic modes employed by children. Rather than perceiving drawings which are not visually realistic as somehow deviant and deficient, adults have to realise the powerful uses of these representations. They need to see that the drawings are the product of systems spontaneously developed by children to answer their own representational requirements. Any one system offered by a child has a relationship to an entire mathematical family of systems. It is important to understand that even very odd-looking drawings produced by children may employ the same systems developed by artists at other times and in other places in the world.

The child's development of representational systems is driven by internal standards and objectives. The immediate task for educators is that they look at what the children produce spontaneously. From there, it is possible to construct appropriate curricula.

The child is continually defining and redefining his or her own world. Drawing plays an important part in this task and guides the construction of an internal model of the world in which such elements as height, width, depth, mass, volume, weight and direction of movement are all elements subordinated within a co-ordinate frame.

The research is now available for teachers to realise the potential of drawing, not only for the development of mathematical skills and understanding, but for the development of cognition in itself.

Proportion: The Measure of Art

Keith Albarn

Introduction

Proportion, number, ratio-geometry, perspective, rhythm and harmony all derive from mankind's early searches for a Grand Design, a pattern that should give shape to our experience and aid our survival. We externalised our concepts through dance, gesture and mark-making and perhaps saw in those early abstractions, similar forms sometimes extracted from dissimilar experiences, our own and others, present and remembered, that would hint at an underlying pattern – a hidden order that informed the cosmos. Our observation of, and feeling for, the circadian rhythms of night and day, the monthly rhythms of moon and menstruation, the movements of the tides, the changing of the seasons, the rhythms, patterns and symmetries in our bodies and those of others and in the natural forms about us, all speak of a complex of relationships that appears to be designed.

As these Great Mysteries are given shape, and as those shapes evolve as general principles, experience leads us to recognise the power of metaphor and analogy, the principles that appear to operate in both the microcosm and the macrocosm and the similarity of relationships in the emotional as well as the practical domain. We recognise that values have a qualitative as well as a quantitative aspect. Such understanding means comprehending structures that lie under the surface of appearances, intra-structures, that give shape to ideas. These intra-structures within ideas are made manifest through the process of notation in gesture, mark or word. As an idea is externalised, it becomes simplified or abstracted through the limitations of the media. Not only does this externalisation of ideas allow for communication and a sharing of these abstract models with others, but in 'putting it out there' we are each able to communicate with the concept alone, as a new part of our own phenomenal world. Thus, we reinforce, by the recognition of certain shared and common intra-structure, the existence of patterns in the world of which we are part. We need to be aware of these patterns in order to understand them and to survive. They are multi-layered, extending to the surface reality of the mundane consciousness from deep down in the unconscious, and in the very fabric of our being and in the being of 'It All'.

Our evolving sense of proportion was assisted by the perceived mechanics of movement, rotation, leverage and, particularly, balance, felt in the use of our bodies and observed in nature. This understanding led to the application of those principles in the development of our extensors: tools and weapons. These developments gave us a sense of individual power over others and over the environment, and thus a greater sense of self-identity and a dawning sense of semi-autonomy. Nevertheless in all cultures there has been retained an understanding that

> a living organism or social body is not an aggregate of elementary parts or elementary processes – it is an integrated hierarchy of semi-autonomous sub-wholes, consisting of sub-sub-wholes and so on. Thus the functional units on every level of the hierarchy are *double-faced* as it were: they act as wholes when facing downwards, as parts when facing upwards.
>
> Thomas, 1974

Many ideas of value lie dormant within the dynamic structures and processes of communication, awaiting discovery. Communication can be seen as the active principle of our model of the cosmos. The act of communication affects that which we are communicating, ideas are in a sense our only reality. It is they that give shape to our sense of being.

Number

Number was of prime importance in patterning our early existence, giving shape to our activities and shaping our constructions. In ancient Greece, the Pythagoreans decreed that, 'Everything was arranged according to Number.' Later, Plato in the Seventh Letter of the *Timaeus* states, 'All things . . . received their shapes from the Ordering One through the action of idea and number'. The fundamental order, the original meaning of cosmos, was of correspondence between the macrocosmos, It All, given the number 10, and the microcosmos, of man, numbered 5. The temple was a manifestation of the relationship as a proportional mean between the two.

From our own hands (eight fingers and two thumbs) sprang the base of ten (digits) and we can now see how from within the microcosmic notion grew a self-generating model that came to order all experience and for many is *the* experience of order (cosmos).

Consider the number array:

0, 1, 2, 3, 4, 5, 6, 7, 8, 9, <u>10</u>, 11, 12, 13, 14, 15, 16, 17, 18, 19, <u>20</u>, 21, etc.

If we now 'reduce' all double digits by adding them together until they produce a single digit array we generate:

0, 1, 2, 3, 4, 5, 6, 7, 8, <u>9</u>, 1, 2, 3, 4, 5, 6, 7, 8, <u>9</u>, 1, 2, 3, etc.

This is a repeat of the array (1–8) punctuated by 9s (other than at the beginning, 0).
We can 'cast out the nines'.

Within each array (1–8) we can see that pairs of numbers added together make 9 and that those pairs are disposed symmetrically around 4 and 5.

$$4 + 5 = 9, \quad 3 + 6 = 9, \quad 2 + 7 = 9, \quad 1 + 8 = 9 \quad \text{or:}$$

1234	1r	also	even numbers	2468	2r
+ 8765	8r		odd numbers	+ 7531	7r
9999	9r			9999	9r

where *r* indicates a reduced number.

This pattern in numbers becomes even clearer when we square each number in the series and again, where necessary, reduce them.

$$1^2, 2^2, 3^2, 4^2 \ . \ 5^2, 6^2, 7^2, 8^2$$
$$= \ 1 \ , \ 4 \ , \ 9 \ , 7r \ . \ 7r \ , 9r \ , 4r \ , 1r$$

Extracting the nines leaves:

$$147 \ . \ 741$$

which if subtracted from

	999		999
i.e.	− 147	or	− 741
gives	852		258

Note that, in each case, the 3, 6 and 9 from the original array (1–9) do not appear.

The three clusters of three numbers (147, 852 and 369 or their mirror equivalents) encompass all numbers 1–9.

These can be re-arranged to form the first of a series of Magic Squares, each related to a specific planet (Nasr, 1964). The first one is the square of Saturn, the sum of whose diagonals, vertical and horizontal columns add up to 15.

The magic square is either constructed by:

```
        1
    4       2
7       5       3
    8       6
        9
```

The three groups
are then shuffled
into place by
moving the
1, 7, 3 and 9

4	9	2
3	5	7
8	1	6

or by remembering a visual overlay which fills the 3 × 3 square starting with 1 in the centre bottom line, as shown in Figure 1.

Figure 1

Within these squares were reminders of key notions (Critchlow, 1976) e.g.

4	9	2
3	5	7
8	1	6

The numbers given emphasis add up to 28, the lunar cycle and they leave 1, 3, 5, 8 which were used in the classification of natural phenomena.

Each planet had an associated square with its own particular characteristics and value as a source of hidden knowledge.

One series central to any discussion of proportion is the Fibonacci Series which over its length progresses ever nearer to the *golden ratio*, a proportion, 1 : 1.618 034 . . . , much used in the art and architecture of the Greek, Gothic and Renaissance periods.

The Fibonacci Series:

$$0, 1, 1, 2, 3, 5, 8, 13, 21, 34, 55, 89, 144, \text{ etc.,}$$

can be reduced where necessary to produce

$$0, 1, 1, 2, 3, 5, 8, 4, 3, 7, 1, 8, 9, \text{ etc.}$$

If continued, it will repeat after 24 digits.

We can now take alternate numbers and create two series.

$$\text{First:} \quad 1, \quad 2, \quad 5, \quad 4, \quad 7, \quad 8$$

with the pairs 1 and 8, 2 and 7, 5 and 4, the 'hinge', all adding up to 9.

$$\text{Second:} \quad 1, \quad 3, \quad 8, \quad 3, \quad 1$$

where we see the reflection around 8.

9 is seen again punctuating the array, indicating here reflection or repetition.

If we start the series with 3:

$$0, 3, 3, 6, 9, 15, 24, 39, 63, 102, 165, 267, 432, \text{ etc.}$$

and reduce:

$$0, 3, 3, 6, 9, 6, 6, 3, 9, 3, 3, 6, 9, \text{ etc.}$$

the patterns are very clear and amplify the 3, 6, 9 relationship. We can see that each number generates a characteristic pattern.

Furthermore, if we take adjacent pairs of numbers in the original series we will see the increasing approximation to the golden mean of 1 : 1.618 034 . . .

e.g. $\frac{8}{5} = 1.6$, $\frac{55}{34} = 1.617\,647$, $\frac{144}{89} = 1.617\,975$

The golden mean, described by Luca Pacioli (a friend of Leonardo da Vinci) as 'The Divine Proportion', and by the great mathematician, Kepler, as 'one of the two jewels of Geometry', has already been referred to in this text as perhaps the most influential proportion in the history of art and mathematics. It is most commonly generated from the square or from the pentagon, where $\phi \approx 1.618\,034$, as shown in Figures 2 and 3.

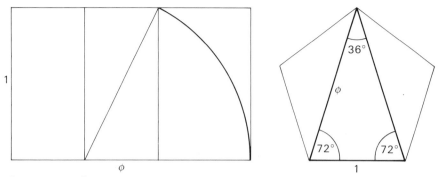

Figures 2 and 3 Two constructions of the golden mean, from the square and the pentagon, where $\phi = 1.618\,034\ldots$

It appears throughout art and nature, including the human body in the ratio of the total height of the average adult male to the height of his navel[1], in the ratio of the three bones of the middle finger (the longer being the sum of the other two) and in the proportion of a 'good looking face' (see Figures 4 and 5 and the exercises at the end of this chapter).

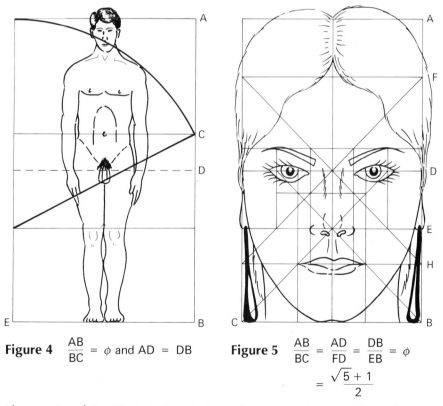

Figure 4 $\dfrac{AB}{BC} = \phi$ and $AD = DB$

Figure 5 $\dfrac{AB}{BC} = \dfrac{AD}{FD} = \dfrac{DB}{EB} = \phi$

$\qquad\qquad = \dfrac{\sqrt{5} + 1}{2}$

Figures 4 and 5 The bold lines indicate the construction as in Figure 2

[1]The ratio in a newborn child is $1 : 1$.

The Ancients used an approximation, seen also in the Fibonacci Series, as an ideal human form of $\frac{8}{5}$ for the male and of $\frac{5}{3}$ for the female.

If we now look at a variant of the full Fibonacci Series as a fractioning series, we see that it is a simple process of accretion (gnomonic growth or in nature, homothetic growth) (Ghyka, 1946; D'Arcy Thompson, 1917).

$$\frac{1}{1}, \frac{1}{2}, \frac{2}{3}, \frac{3}{5}, \frac{5}{8}, \frac{8}{13}, \frac{13}{21}, \frac{21}{34}, \frac{34}{55}, \frac{55}{89}, \frac{89}{144}, \text{etc.}$$

We will find a correspondence to this series with branching in plants. Phyllotaxis is the measure which arises from the need to maximise the exposure to light of each new leaf during growth. The numerator is the number of times we circle the stem and the denominator is the number of shoots, thorns or branches we pass through. Each species tends to have a characteristic ratio, $\frac{2}{5}$ for the hawthorn, apple and oak, $\frac{1}{3}$ for the sedges, beech and hazel, $\frac{3}{8}$ for the plantain, poplar and pear and $\frac{5}{13}$ for leeks, willow and almond. From this evidence, (Stevens, 1974) it is not then very surprising to see that in the intersecting curves made by seeds in the head of the ripe sunflower we see, depending on the species, $\frac{13}{21}, \frac{21}{34}, \frac{34}{55}$ or $\frac{89}{144}$. Similar observations of fir cones will elicit ratios of $\frac{5}{8}$ or $\frac{8}{13}$, etc.

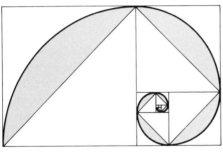

Figure 6   **Figure 7**

Figures 6 and 7   Logarithmic spiral of the nautilus shell (Figure 6) compared with the Archimedes spiral (Figure 7)

Geometry

As in the unfolding of number from singularity, origin and oneness, we see interweaving patterns and continuities of rhythm linking the separate identities of each quantity with quality, retaining a sense of the single wholeness. Thus, as a point with zero dimensions moves to make a line with one dimension, a line moves to make a plane with two dimensions, a plane moves to make a solid with three dimensions, and a solid moves to make a hyper-solid of four dimensions, and so on, we move into the central arena of geometry (see Figure 8).

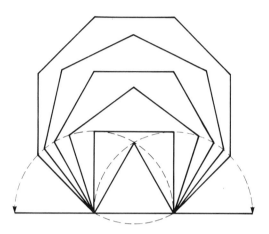

Figure 8   The unfolding of polygons, triangle, square, pentagon, hexagon, heptagon and octagon

We must begin with the circle generated from a single point. It is the prime figure whose circumference is the most economic of planar space and from which all geometry sprang. It is the origin and the equivalent of oneness in number. The origin of the use of stick and thong, the compass, to describe circles and then to construct, using the same methods, a multitude of patterns and polygons is buried in the mists of time. The encircling dance, conversation around the camp fire, the encircling horizon, the arc of the heavens, the rings in the pool, ... all must have reinforced the significance of this form and developed the processes and applications employing the circle. The orientation of the site for the temple was made possible by the simple circle whose circumference would be crossed by the longest shadow cast by the sun from the central pole denoting its rising in the east and its setting in the west. Connect these points, and using greater intersecting circles, mark at the points of intersection the north and south (Burckhardt, 1967). Thus the temple recorded and predicted the passage of the seasons.

The spatial equivalent of the circle is the sphere, the most symmetrical and economic form for enclosing a given volume, hence its appearence in nature, from the planets to the bubbles in the air. The sphere's multi-directional symmetry encapsulated our unfolding model of space–time, as experienced from earth, right up to the beginning of the twentieth century. In clusters, spheres prefigure all the Platonic and Archimedean solids making patterns in space. Four spheres in contact with each other, the greatest number possible, form the points of the Tetrahedron. The next most economic array involves six spheres with each sphere touching four others to form the octahedral grouping and so on (Critchlow, 1969). We can draw a circle and then with the same radius, intersect the circumference to mark off six points. Joining every other one produces the triangle, the simplest and strongest of the polygons having only three sides and no chords. (As with the instrument of the same name!)

The triangle is the beginning of the unfolding of the polygons and is seen as the Soul. The sum of its angles is 180° (*9r*). As a lattice it fills a given space completely and, with rotation and reflection, it provides a valuable basis for the decoration of a surface (Weyl, 1952).

Figure 9   Gnomonic growth, ratio 2 : 1

Some triangles became much used and thus gained in value. Amongst these special triangles was the 3, 4, 5 right-angled triangle, formed from a rope with twelve knots, as in Figure 10. This 'sacred triangle' guaranteed not only a right angle but did so uniquely by the use of the ratio 3 : 4 : 5 (which reduces to 3).

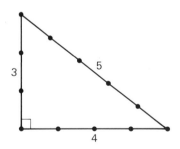

Figure 10   Sacred triangle

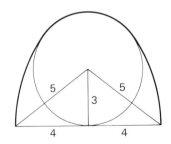

Figure 11   Construction for a Persian dome

The isosceles triangle that is formed within the pentagon was much used as the ratio of the short to the longer side is 1 : 1.618 034 or the golden section (see Figure 3). It has two angles of 72° and one of 36°, all of which reduce to 9, again. It is also a self-replicating figure (see Figure 12).

Figure 12   Self-replication

In space, four equilateral triangles form the prime solid, the tetrahedron (see Figure 13a), the first of the five Platonic solids (see Figure 13). The tetrahedron is also the fundamental form in nature, as carbon atoms are arranged in tetrahedra in diamond, the purest form of carbon. In ancient times the tetrahedron represented fire. The second Platonic solid is the octahedron (air, see Figure 13b). The third is the cube which represented earth (Figure 13c). The icosahedron (water, the fourth solid, see Figure 13d) is formed of twenty equilateral triangles and by spanning opposite edges no less than fifteen ϕ rectangles can be generated. This is the largest of the regular, triangulated solids and it held a great attraction for geometers and artists alike. The fifth Platonic solid is the dodecahedron (cosmos, see Figure 13e), which has a structure closely related to that of the icosahedron.

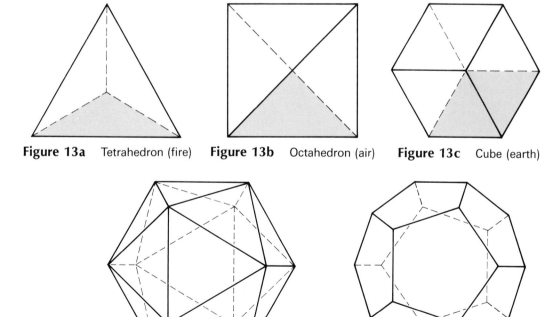

Figure 13a   Tetrahedron (fire)   **Figure 13b**   Octahedron (air)   **Figure 13c**   Cube (earth)

Figure 13d   Icosahedron (water)   **Figure 13e**   Dodecahedron (cosmos)

Figures 13a–e   The five Platonic solids

From the triangle, matter, unfolds the square with its four right-angled corners, four sides and plane-filling symmetries.

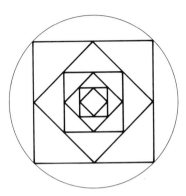

Figure 14   √2 ratio of gnomonic growth

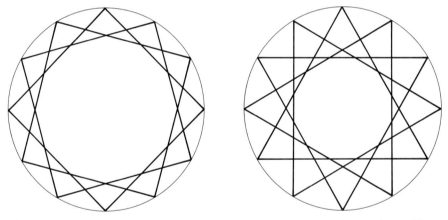

Figure 15   Dodecagonal stars that link the square and triangle, much used in Islamic patterns

Projected into three dimensions the square becomes the cube (earth) and stands four square (with six sides!). Despite its inherent structural instability, unlike the tetrahedron with its tepee-like form, the cubic lattice features strongly in our buildings, due to the use of post and lintel constructions. The cube is the first space-filling solid of the Platonic solids and is alone in having square faces. It is easily visualised and drawn, hence its value in the development of drawing systems. It dominates our conceptual models, as the Cartesian coordinates, as much as it dominates our constructed environment. The manipulation of the square and cube, both being the first figures in their respective dimensions to have a chord, gave rise to a fuller understanding of the irrational numbers (see Figure 16).

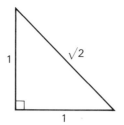

Figure 16 √2 triangle

It was from the use of these figures that we gained our measure of plane and of volume. These uses led to extensions of the figures on the plane and in space employing 'special' rectangles based upon either ratio or number. The former, built by point and arc, were known as 'dynamic' (see Figure 17). The latter, built of numbers of squares, were known as 'static' (see Figure 18).

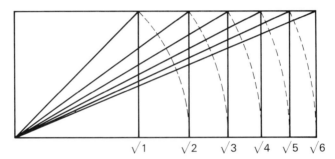

Figure 17 Dynamic rectangles

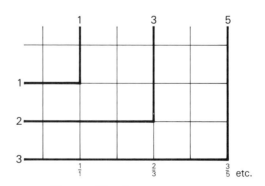

Figure 18 Static rectangles

There is, of course, one special construction that leads to the golden rectangle of 'sublime proportion', 1 : 1.618 034 (see Figure 2). This construction will lead to all manner of rhythmic extensions in which the homothetic growth patterns are synonymous with many forms in nature: the nautilus shell, the horn of the ram, etc., and as we have seen, within the human body (see Figures 5, 6, and 19).

31

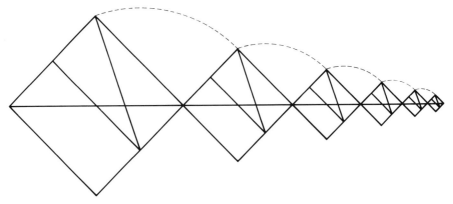

Figure 19   The growth of squares by the ratio ϕ (golden mean)

So frequent is its appearance in nature (inevitable, given the determinants of space-time) and in our own physiology and psychology that it is not surprising that scientists, artists and architects throughout the ages have been guided consciously or unconsciously by it in their pursuit of the ideal proportion[1] (see Figures 20–3).

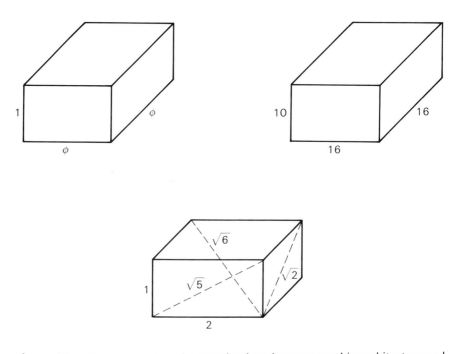

Figure 20   Some examples of proportion in volume as used in architecture and furniture through the ages

---

[1] For Leonardo da Vinci, the great artist and inventor of the fifteenth century, proportion was of great significance 'not only . . . in numbers and measurement but also in sounds, weights, positions and in whatsoever power there may be.'

Figure 21 *St Jerome* – unfinished, Leonardo de Vinci

Figure 22   *Parade* (Seurat), harmonic division

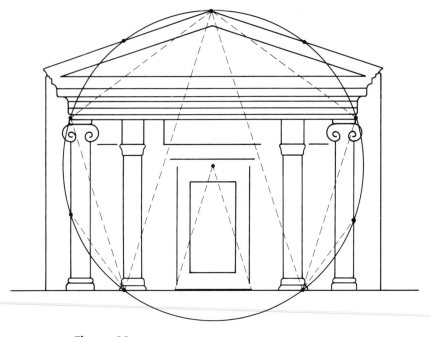

Figure 23   Egyptian temple at Mira (after Moessel)

We can now turn our attention to the five-sided pentagon (man) already referred to earlier in conjunction with the golden mean. This polygon has so many intriguing aspects that it remains to this day a 'magic' shape with occult implications. It is one of the most common forms in biological and primitive zoological structures (see Figures 25 and 27). Its construction requires a little more effort than the triangle or the square and is achieved by sub-dividing the radius of a circle, by drawing arcs to intersect its circumference and then joining these points to one another around the circumference to create the sides. (For a full description see p. 106.) It does not plane-fill although a net of pentagons can be folded with interesting results. Indeed, a net of twelve pentagons will produce the ultimate regular polyhedron of the Platonic solids (the only one to use the pentagon), the dodecahedron (cosmos), which relates to the icosahedron (water) with its four clusters of five triangles and its internal ϕ rectangles described earlier.

Figure 24   Single rope

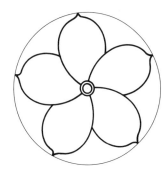

Figure 25   Flower

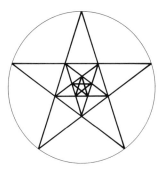

Figure 26   Homothetic growth

Figure 27   Starfish

If five, and the pentagon, are the number and polygon most associated with biological forms then six, and the hexagon, are the number and polygon of crystalline solids (the snowflake, basalt, the honeycomb, etc.). The hexagon has two chords of different lengths (see Figure 30) and, with its simple construction using the arc of the radius of a given circle to mark off in six simple divisions of the circumference its six sides, it is a rich tool for generating plane-filling repeat patterns (see Figures 28 and 32). Such patterns with triangles or diamonds within the hexagons may give an illusion of depth, of illusionary cubes. They are often used in buildings which are based upon the cube or its extensions, thus drawing together the relationship of two or three dimensions in visual harmony (see Figure 31).

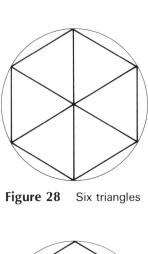

Figure 28   Six triangles

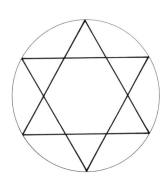

Figure 29   Shield of David

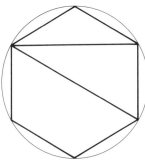

Figure 30 $\sqrt{3}$ ratio

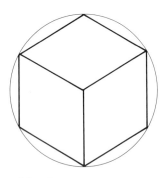

Figure 31   Three diamonds or a cube?

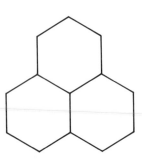

Figure 32   The honeycomb tessellation

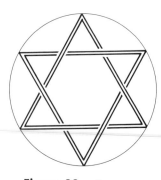

Figure 33   Two ropes

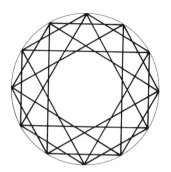
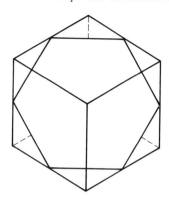

Figure 34 Dodecagon with two hexagons, three squares, six $\sqrt{3}$ rectangles

Figure 35 Hexagon as cross-section of a cube

In this brief review of polygons from triangle to dodecahedron we have not, so far, commented on the seven- or the eleven-sided figures. Suffice it to say that of these two, only the seven-sided heptagon has any real significance and that is more in relation to number than geometry: the seven days of the week and the visible planets. Nevertheless, it is worth noting the link between the circle and the seven- and eleven-sided polygons through the important ratio π or $\frac{22}{7}$. If we know the radius of a given circle, we can calculate its circumference or area using this ratio.

Proportion

The manifestation of significant proportion through geometry in all man's artifacts, from ancient to modern times, not only ensured some semblance of order within the constructed environment, of harmony between that environment and the world about us, but also ensured that the making and thinking of man were read as a realisation of part of the greater plan, the Grand Design. Vitruvius, the Roman architect wrote in his chapter on 'Symmetry in Temples and in the Human Body' from his *Ten Books on Architecture*:

> Since nature has designed the human body so that its members are duly proportioned to the frame as a whole, it appears that the Ancients had good reason for their rule that in perfect buildings the different members must be in exact symmetrical relations to the whole general scheme.

One man[1] who has addressed these issues in this century is Le Corbusier, the great French architect and artist who sought a more meaningful and unifying system of measure. Such a system would, he felt 'unite, co-ordinate, bring into

---

[1]Another is the painter Paul Klee whose concerns were parallel, as seen in his more intuitive approach towards a 'cosmological vision' in *Notebooks, Volume One, The Thinking Eye*, published by Lund and Humphries, 1961.

harmony, the work which is at present divided and disjointed by reason of the existence of two virtually incompatible systems'. He considered the imperial system to be 'steadfast in its attachment to the human body but atrociously difficult to handle', the metric as, 'indifferent to the stature of man and devoid of personality'. He also felt 'nothing that is built, constructed, divided into lengths, widths or volumes, has yet enjoyed the advantage of a measure equivalent to that possessed by music' . . . musical notation. He did recognise that in the work of the Ancients, the concepts of measurement 'were eternal and enduring, precious because they linked to the human person. The names of their tools were elbow (cubit), finger (digit), thumb (inch), foot, pace and so forth . . . they were infinitely rich and subtle because they formed part of the mathematics of the human body, gracious, elegant and firm, the source of the harmony which moves us, beauty.'

These quotations are taken from his book *The Modulor* in which he sets out the principles of his new system of measure. It is a system he applied in his architecture and painting and which influenced many of his own and ensuing generations. The initial registered trade mark for the modulor (later modified and elaborated) was of a man with one arm raised above his head, set in a grid of modulor measure, as shown in Figure 36.

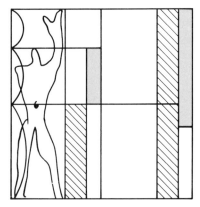

Figure 36   The registered trademark for the Modulor by Le Corbusier. Reprinted by permission of Faber and Faber Ltd from *The Modulor* by Le Corbusier

The measure of his ideal man was 113 units to the navel, 183 units to the top of the head and 226 units to the tips of the fingers of his raised hand.

1 The grid furnishes three measures: 113, 70, 43 (in centimetres in a relationship ϕ or golden section).
   The Fibonacci series furnishes $43 + 70 = 113$, or $113 - 70 = 43$.
   Added together, they give $113 + 70 = 183$, $113 + 70 + 43 = 226$.

2 These three measures (113, 183, 226) define the occupation of space by a man 6 feet in height.

3 The measure 113 furnishes the golden mean 70 which starts off a new series called the Red series: 4, 6, 10, 16, 27, 43, 70, 113, 183, 296, etc. The measure 226 (2×113, the double unit) furnishes the golden mean 140 : 86, which starts off the second series, called the Blue series: 13, 20, 33, 53, 86, 140, 226, 366, 592, etc.

Le Corbusier, 1961

The modulor series is not strictly a mathematical series, but a set of measures. As a result of the conversion between metric and imperial (1.75 m and 6 feet as the 'ideal man') there is an irregularity in the series.

Even more recently we see in the teachings and work of Buckminster Fuller (Marks, 1960), the American engineer (inventor of the Geodesic Dome, shown in Figure 37, and tensegrity structures, amongst many other things of 'principle'), another multi-talented polymath who in his own inimitable use of words: 'Set out . . . to seek for the greatest meanings as well as for the family of generalised principles governing the realisation of their optimum significance to humanity – aboard our sun-circling planet earth.' He saw the task as 'predominantly metaphysical, for it is how to get all humanity to educate itself swiftly enough to generate spontaneous social behaviour that will avoid extinction'. More than most he deplored the 'hyperspecialisation in socio-economic functioning that has come to preclude important, popular philosophic considerations'.

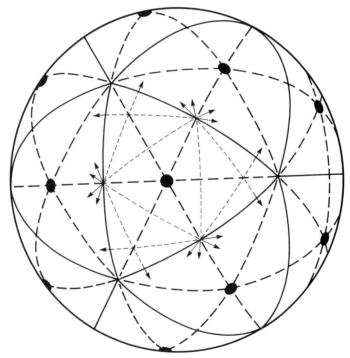

Figure 37   The 'Great Circles' and the 'Alpha Particle'. The smallest triangle is the 'Schwarz' triangle and is the smallest repeating element to equi-divide the sphere's surface. This triangle is hinted at by Plato and called by Buckminster Fuller the 'alpha particle'. It is a spherical right-angled triangle which divides the sphere 120 times. It is defined by the 31 great circles which also define the spherical projections of all five Platonic solids. The finest lines (arrowed) indicate the route of the circles. Where the heavy dotted lines intersect the large dots define the dodecahedron and the solid lines the icosahedron. Thus this spherical geometry used by Buckminster Fuller for his Geodesic Domes links with the Platonic tradition

Adapted with permission of Macmillan Publishing Company from *Synergetics* by R. Buckminster Fuller. Copyright © 1975 by R. Buckminster Fuller

His exploration and use of number and geometry as both tools and metaphors for solving very practical problems with great elegance, and for gaining insights through such studies into the workings of the cosmos are a demonstration of the vitality that still exists in geometrics, a tradition that was almost 'swept away by the Age of Reason', 'Polyhedra and Pentagrams, being proven useful after all.'[1]

This century, the detailed scientific studies of natural phenomena have increasingly confirmed the quantitative aspect of proportion, ratio and harmonics as intuited by the Ancients from their manipulation of number and general observation of nature. However, the qualitative aspect has not yet been fully re-integrated into either art or mathematics, let alone into a commonly-held structure of values. Perhaps in the last half of the twentieth century we are now recognising the need to cease the unthinking exploitation of our habitat and to live in harmony with the Grand Design. There is an urgent need to redevelop a commonly shared cosmology based upon the new state of knowledge and growing awareness, a model that will inform the qualitative as well as the quantitative aspects of our value structures.

We need a sense of proportion!

EXERCISES

Most will require graph paper and tracing paper (or detail paper) and a writing instrument.

1 *The Body*
Draw, measure and number the proportions of yourself, relations and acknowledged beauties of the opposite sex. Pay particular attention to the ratio of total height to height of navel, the ratio between the sub-division of the index finger and the proportions in different faces (full frontal views). Do the good-looking measure up to the 'Divine Proportion' of Figures 4 and 5?

2 *The Face*
Map the key facial features on a grid, then play games with the grid (distort it) plotting the face onto each new grid and see not only how the shape changes but how changes in proportion indicate changes in personality.

This is shown in Figure 38.

---

[1] As Arthur L. Loeb comments wryly in his preface to *Synergetics* by Buckminster Fuller, 'This book is truly cosmic in its scope and highly individualistic in its style . . .'

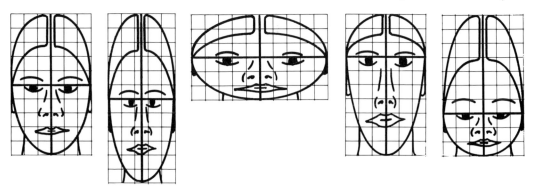

Figure 38   (after D'Arcy Thompson)

3 *A Fish*

Consider a fish, or any organism, in profile and map that on to a simple grid. Then change the proportions by distorting the grid, as in Figure 39. Note how the 'species' changes. Use anamorphic views to gain similar effects (and explore with curved reflective surfaces).

Describe the geometry at work here, and how we read a circle when all we see is an ellipse.

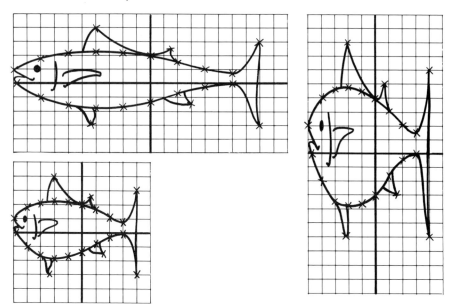

Figure 39   (after D'Arcy Thompson)

4 *Nature*

Draw, measure and number the spirals in the head of a sunflower, in fir cones, in the patterns of branching, in petal forms, etc. Note the recurrence of certain numbers and see Figures 6, 7, 25 and 27. Five is common in flower heads and simple organisms, why is it not found in the inorganic forms of crystals?

5 *A Painting*

Using a reproduction of a painting, for example, from the Renaissance, trace the major features in the composition and then seek out the geometry of the proportions, as in Figure 22. Produce your own composition using geometry, and particularly that involving the dynamic rectangles, to create a harmonious whole.

6 *Architecture*

Take the elevation (or a photograph) of a Greek or Roman temple or a building by Le Corbusier and analyse its proportions. Then, design your own temple based upon root two, root three, or the golden ratio using only compass and straight-edge and consider the proportion of its volume(s) in space (see Figures 17–20).

Take the basic elements of your own or another design and change the proportions – can you improve it?

7 *Fibonacci Series*

Take the Fibonacci Series, reduced as described on p. 24, and work through the patterns generated by the split series using all the numbers 1–8 (1, 1, 2, etc and 3, 3, 6 etc are touched upon in the text). Explore the repeats and reflections and then plot them as a spiral graph and see again how each number has a distinct character. Use a colour code to enhance the patterns you produce.

Use the proportions within the series to create geometric equivalents of natural forms and note how close they are to the golden mean (e.g. $\frac{144}{89} = 1.617\,977\,5\ldots$ as against $1.618\,034\ldots$ for ϕ).

8 *Temple*

Now design the decorations for your temple outlined in Exercise 6 and choreograph a suitable ritual for a twentieth-century Pythagorean.

Perspective Drawings

4

William Wynne Willson

Introduction

A maze picture

We are all used to pictures which show us things drawn in perspective. Here, for example, is a scene from a computer maze game.

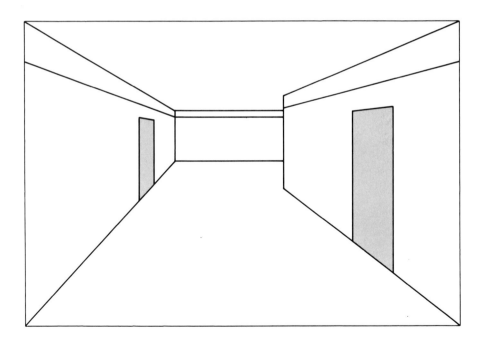

Figure 1

An adolescent looking at this on the computer screen would have no difficulty in telling you that it shows the view down a passage between two walls, with doors on either side. If you walk to the end, the passage goes round the corner to the right.

This picture is made up of just 17 straight lines drawn on a flat piece of paper or computer screen, together with a little shading for the doors. How is it able to convey this sensation of space? Why does it make you see it as a solid three-dimensional scene rather than a flat two-dimensional pattern? How is it that you can interpret it, seeing that the door on the left is further away than the door on the right, but that they are both the same size? The aim of this chapter is to answer such questions as these, to describe some of the simple rules which enable perspective pictures to be drawn (either by people or by computers) and to use some geometry to explain the rules and show where they come from.

Straight lines

The most basic rule for perspective is that the picture of a straight line should always be a straight line! This may seem obvious, but remember that, by comparison, the picture of a circle will generally not be a circle. A circular coin lying on the floor with look something like this:

Figure 2a

and a bicycle wheel will look like this:

Figure 2b

If you think about the door on the right of the passage in Figure 1 its real shape is a rectangle. The top and bottom and the two sides are really straight lines, and these appear as straight lines in the picture. On the other hand, the corners of the actual door would really be right angles, but these angles in the picture are certainly not drawn as right angles (see Figure 3). The rectangular shape of the door looks, in the picture, to be quite distorted.

Figure 3

The great majority of pictures show scenes as they would appear to someone looking more or less horizontally. Of course there are exceptions to this: a view from the bottom of a skyscraper looking up can be very dramatic, and an aerial photo of a house can be very useful. However, it will make things simpler if we ignore these possibilities at present, and just consider what happens when you draw a perspective picture showing what you see when you are standing upright and your gaze is level. In this case there is a second simple rule: lines which are actually vertical appear in the picture as vertical lines. This is illustrated by the sides of the doors and the ends of the walls in the maze picture.

(*Note*: We are using the word *vertical* here in two different ways. When talking about the side of the door, or a flagpole or a plumb-line, it means at right angles to the horizontal ground. When we are talking about lines in the picture it means straight up and down the page or screen. This should not be too confusing; both ways of using the word are familiar, and it should always be clear from the context which meaning is involved in any particular case.)

Next, consider the top and bottom of the back wall shown in the maze picture. These are horizontal lines running straight across the field of view from left to right. Once again the rule is simple: these appear as horizontal lines running from left to right in the picture.

Now, the top and bottom of the left hand wall are also in reality horizontal lines, but in the picture they are drawn sloping. This is because they are pointing away from the viewer. The bottom one, which is below eye level, slopes up as it moves away from you in the picture, while the top one, above eye level, slopes down. This agrees with the familiar fact that as things move away from you they appear to get smaller. The height of the walls remains the same, so the drawing of the top and the bottom of the left-hand wall in the picture must be closer to each other at the far end of the passage than they are at the near end.

There is more to be said about this. Lines which approach one another in a drawing can be extended to meet. Extending the tops and bottoms of the walls and doors in the maze picture gives the result shown in Figure 4 on p. 46.

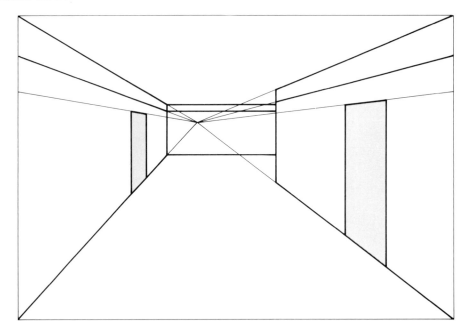

Figure 4

You will see that all these lines meet at a single point! This is because the lines which they represent in the passage are all in the same direction, that is to say, they are parallel to one another. Points like this at which the lines representing a set of parallel lines meet, are known as *vanishing points*. In this particular case not only are the lines parallel, they are also horizontal: the effect of this is that the vanishing point at which they meet is at eye level.

To illustrate these ideas further consider Figure 5.

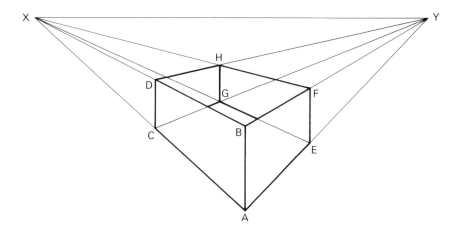

Figure 5

This is a 'three-quarter view' looking down on a large open cardboard box, which sits on a flat level floor. The four vertical edges (AB, CD, EF and GH) appear as vertical lines in the picture. The edges AC, BD, FH and EG are parallel horizontal lines (although part of EG is hidden); when extended as shown these meet at a vanishing point, X. In the same way, the parallel horizontal lines AE, BF, DH and CG also meet at a vanishing point, Y. In the maze picture the edges of the left- and right-hand walls and the tops of the doors were all in the same direction, and so the lines representing them in the picture all met in a single vanishing point. In the box picture, two separate sets of horizontal parallel lines are represented. Since these two sets are in different directions, their vanishing points, X and Y, are different. But, because these edges of the box are horizontal, both X and Y are at eye level. So, the line joining X and Y is the line which goes straight across the picture at eye level. We feel that we are looking down on the box because in this drawing the line XY is above the box.

It may be useful here to summarise the rules so far:

1 Straight lines in space appear as straight lines on paper.

2 Vertical lines in space appear as vertical lines on paper.

3 Horizontal lines straight across the field of view appear as horizontal lines across the paper.

4 Other sets of parallel lines in space appear as lines meeting at a point on paper: such a point is called a *vanishing point*.

5 A horizontal set of lines in space has its vanishing point on the line across the paper which represents eye level.

EXERCISES

Here are a few ideas for you to try out either on yourself or on your pupils.

1 Find a convenient window on the ground floor. Put a large cardboard box on a chair outside at an angle to the window and about three feet from it. Now sit inside looking out and be prepared to draw on the window with a (washable!) overhead projector pen. (You may prefer to fix a blank overhead projector transparency to the window with sellotape; the transparency should be at the right level for you to see the box through it.) Hold your head very steady about one foot away from the transparency and close one eye. Carefully trace the outline of the box on to the transparency with an OHP pen. This should give you a picture recognisably like the one discussed above.

2 Figure 6 on p. 48 shows three flagpoles in the desert. Two are the same height as each other, but the third is longer. By adding suitable lines find the odd flagpole, and chop a bit off the top to make it the same height as the others.

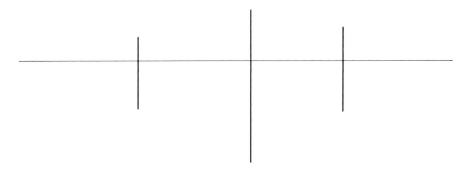

Figure 6

3 By adding suitable lines to the maze picture, show that the two doors are the same width.

History

Having described the basic rules for perspective drawing, we turn to look briefly at how these developed and have been used by artists throughout human history.

Before perspective

Figure 7   Egyptian Wall Painting: about 2000 BC

Some of the earliest pictures to survive are those on the walls of the tombs in the Valley of the Kings in Egypt. They are vivid paintings which retain their bright colours and give a lively idea of what it was like to be king of Upper Egypt in 2000 BC. But they make no attempt to give the impression of solid figures; the images, lacking perspective, seem completely flat, as seen in Figure 7.

Until fairly recently, little was known about classical Greek and Roman painting. Discoveries during the present century have revealed pictures showing that the Romans knew the rules of perspective. Figure 8 shows a painting from a villa in Pompeii which had remained buried since the first century AD and shows fully developed perspective.

Figure 8   Fresco in "The House of Mysteries", Pompeii: before AD 100

With the fall of the Roman Empire the rules of perspective, like many other elements of classical tradition, were forgotten. Just 1000 years later than the Pompeii picture, the Bayeux tapestry adopts a style very like the Egyptians. The extract shown in Figure 9 on p. 50 has a building in the background. You will notice that the side wall on the left of the picture is drawn as though the viewer was on its left, and the wall on the right requires the viewer to be on its right; meanwhile, the dying King Edward the Confessor is viewed from the centre.

49

Figure 9   From the Bayeux Tapestry: about AD 1080

Brunelleschi and his successors

During the Renaissance, the rules of perspective were rediscovered by the Florentine artist and architect, Filippo Brunelleschi, who lived from 1377 to 1446. From the fifteenth century onwards knowledge of it spread rapidly through Europe. The view of a courtyard of a house in Delft shown in Plate 4.1 was painted by Pieter de Hooch in the middle of the seventeenth century. It is carefully constructed, with the rectangular tiles in the foreground providing strong horizontal lines running across and away from the viewer. Some of the latter have been highlighted to show the vanishing point.

It is interesting to note that the eye level is at about elbow height for the two adults in the picture, but above the little girl's head. Perhaps the artist wanted to show a child's view of the scene. The positioning of the vanishing point is also carefully contrived to lead the eye through the archway into the hidden courtyard behind. Clearly de Hooch was trying to make us curious about who is out there beyond the open door.

During the seventeenth and eighteenth centuries it was taken for granted in European art that pictures should be painted in perspective. Later, in the nineteenth century, it is worth noting that Turner, the great innovator, remained faithful to perspective. Indeed, he was appointed Professor of Perspective at the Royal Academy in 1807, and gave lectures on the subject throughout the following twenty years.

After perspective

In the twentieth century artists have felt free to ignore the rules of perspective if they chose to. Picasso's *Mandolin and Guitar* (1924) exploits the idea of using perspectives appropriate to differing viewpoints in different parts of the picture (see Plate 4.2).

Other people have used perspective in other ways. Salvador Dali was fond of long perspective views; *Christ of St John of the Cross* (1951), shown in Plate 4.3, is typical.

One recent artist who was evidently intrigued by perspective was the Dutchman, M. C. Escher. His lithograph *Drawing Hands* (1948) is one of a number of examples of pictures in which he exploits the idea of contrasting three-dimensional and two-dimensional images (see Figure 10).

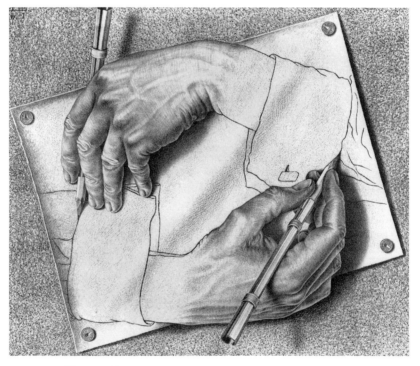

Figure 10　Drawing hands: M. C. Escher, 1948
© 1990 M. C. Escher Heirs/Cordon Art-Baarn-Holland
Collection Haags Gemeentemuseum – The Hague

Here the hands, which are shown in perspective and appear convincingly solid, are drawing the cuffs which seem to stay on the paper. A further twist is added by making the piece of paper on which the hands are drawing appear clearly three-dimensional (it is curling up at the edges); yet, of course, the lithograph itself is actually flat.

51

Much of Escher's work reveals an interest in mathematics, the most familiar cases being the tessellations discussed in Chapter 6 of this book. In the 1950s the mathematician Roger Penrose (then a student, but now Professor of Mathematics at Oxford) sent him a drawing of an 'impossible object' which he had invented. Escher responded with his own versions; Figure 11 shows one of them – *Belvedere* (1958).

Figure 11   Belvedere: M. C. Escher, 1958
© 1990 M. C. Escher Heirs/Cordon Art–Baarn–Holland
Collection Haags Gemeentemuseum – The Hague

Take a quick glance at this and you will see a two-storey structure. Closer inspection shows that it is impossible to reconcile the upper balcony with the lower one (see Exercise 6 on p. 54). Notice too, that the 'object' held by the youth on the bench in front is also 'impossible'.

Some discussion of 'impossible objects', including the original 'Penrose triangle' can be found in the SMP 11–16 books Y2 and B2.

This short survey of the use of perspective has suggested that after its introduction into western art in the fourteenth century, it dominated the tradition for some 500 years. More recently, it has come to be seen as one of the potential features of a picture, which may be used consistently, but which also may be deliberately distorted to produce particular effects.

EXERCISES

4 Find the vanishing point for Pieter de Hooch's *Woman Peeling Apples* shown in Figure 12.

Figure 12   Woman Peeling Apples: Pieter de Hooch (1629–84)
Reproduced by permission of the Trustees of the Wallace Collection

53

5 Draw in lines running horizontally away from the viewer for Domenico Veneziano's *Miracle of Saint Zenobius* shown in Figure 13. (Note that other pictures by the same fifteenth century artist establish that he knew the rules of perspective!)

Figure 13 The Miracle of Saint Zenobius: Domenico Veneziano, 1442
Reproduced by permission of the Syndics of the Fitzwilliam Museum, Cambridge

6 Investigate the vanishing points in Escher's *Belvedere*.

Geometry

In this section we consider perspective from a geometrical standpoint. First, we look at where the rules come from, then, we apply them to draw slightly more elaborate pictures.

Proving the rules

For the sake of brevity, the word *line* will always mean *straight line* (anything else is a curve). We will also use the word *plane* in its geometrical sense, to mean a completely flat surface, like a stiff piece of cardboard.

In the exercise in which you were encouraged to draw on the window, you had to close one eye. Most of us look at the world through two eyes. Since our eyes are a few centimetres apart they see slightly different views which our brains then combine so that we have the impression of only a single view. But, if you concentrate your attention on something near to you, and alternately close and open each eye, you will be able to tell that these two views are really different. In order to avoid this difficulty, we shall work on the assumption that you keep one eye closed, and talk about the position of *the* eye as though you had only one.

It is well known that light travels in straight lines. Imagine yourself again looking at a cardboard box outside the window, and marking on the window where you see one corner, A, of the box. If your eye is at a point E, light from A will travel along the line AE, and you will mark the point at which this line meets the window. Let's call this point A′. In the same way, if you look at a second corner of the box, B, light from B will travel along the line BE to your eye, and this line will meet the window at a point which we should call B′. This is shown in Figure 14.

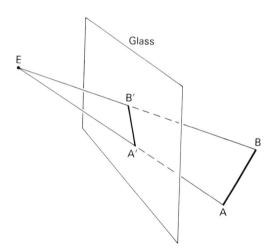

Figure 14

Now there is just one plane going through three points like A, B and E. If you imagine fitting a piece of cardboard through both A and B, you can then rotate it about AB: as you turn it, there would be just one position in which it also goes through E. What is more, the line AB lies entirely in this plane, so the rays of light joining the points of AB to E all lie in this plane. This means that the *picture* of AB which you draw on the window will be where the plane meets the window, and this will be the line A′B′. This argument proves the first rule of perspective, that straight lines in space appear as straight lines on paper.

Now imagine yourself standing between two horizontal railway lines X_1X_2 and Y_1Y_2. Your eye is at E, and you look horizontally straight ahead in the direction of the lines, your line of sight being EF. On a sheet of glass in front of you, you mark where you see the railway lines.

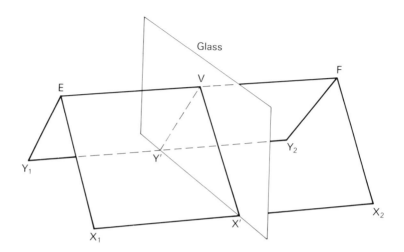

Figure 15

In Figure 15, the points where EF, X_1X_2 and Y_1Y_2 meet the glass are marked as V, X' and Y'. As in the last case, the rays of light reaching you from the line X_1X_2 will all lie in the plane EX_1X_2 and this meets the glass in the line $X'V$. This means that the picture of the line X_1X_2 will be the line $X'V$. In the same way, the picture of the other railway line will be the line $Y'V$. This shows that the two horizontal parallel railway lines appear in the picture as two lines meeting at the vanishing point V.

This completes the proof of Rules 1, 4 and 5, on p. 47. If you are keen to prove Rules 2 and 3, you should be able to do this yourself; the arguments are very similar to those used above.

Drawing a house

The rules of perspective are not complicated, but used with a little ingenuity, they can enable you to draw quite elaborate diagrams. As an example, we consider a traditional house – a rectangular 'box' with a sloping roof.

A drawing for the box part of the house has already been produced in Figure 5, p. 46. We have to add on the roof, and we assume that this should be symmetrical, with the ridge RS parallel to BD and FH, and midway between the wall ABDC and the wall EFHG. The main problem is to decide where R can go.

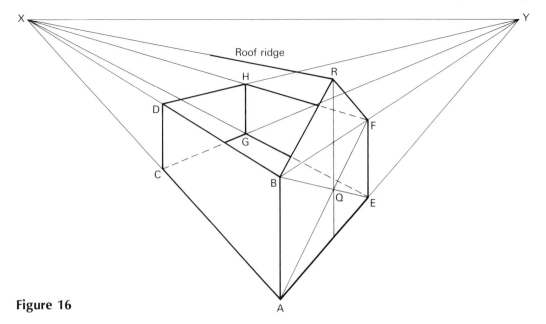

Figure 16

The answer to this is to find the centre of BFEA. If we join BE and AF in the picture, the point of intersection, Q, will be the required centre. (This is because of Rule 1). If we now draw a vertical line through Q, we can choose a point on this to be R. (This is because of Rule 2). Next, because RS is parallel to AC and BD, in the drawing it must go through the vanishing point X. (This is because of Rule 4).

All that remains now is to find the position of S, the other end of the roof ridge. You should be able to do this.

EXERCISES

7 Complete the drawing of the house.

8 On your completed drawing, extend lines FR and HS to meet at Z. Also extend lines RB and SD to meet at W. If all your drawing has been done accurately, then the line WZ will go vertically up the page and pass exactly through X. (This is a consequence of a famous theorem called Desargues' theorem. For a very readable account of this, see W. W. Sawyer, *Prelude to Mathematics*, p. 147.)

9 Find the centre of the floor AEGC of your house and divide the floor into quarters by joining this point to X and Y. Now subdivide each of these quarters by a similar method. This should give the appearance of a tiled floor made up from 16 equal rectangular tiles. (Do it again and you will have a chessboard!)

Computers

Nowadays, in offices and places where drawings are produced, most of the pencils and drawing boards have been replaced by computer screens. This is not surprising since a micro supplied with a good CAD (Computer-Aided Design) package is such a powerful instrument for creating pictures to order. The purpose of the last section of this chapter is to give an idea of how the process of producing perspective pictures on computer screens works. The mathematics involved is simpler than you might expect.

Coordinates on the screen

When drawing computer graphics, we need some way to describe particular points on the screen. This is done by imagining *x*- and *y*-axes such as are drawn on ordinary graph paper, with the *x*-axis running along the bottom of the screen and the *y*-axis up the left-hand edge. The scales for these axes will depend on the model of computer: for the BBC machines which are at present the most commonly found in schools, the *x*-axis is numbered from 0 to 1279 and the *y*-axis from 0 to 1023.

Points are described by giving the *x*-coordinate and *y*-coordinate in order. A typical sequence of instructions to a BBC Micro might be:

10　MODE　4	This warns the Micro that a picture is to be drawn.
20　MOVE　640,512	This moves the 'pen' to the middle of the screen, without leaving a mark.
30　DRAW　960,512	This moves the pen 320 units (that is about a quarter of the screen's width) to the right, drawing in the line.

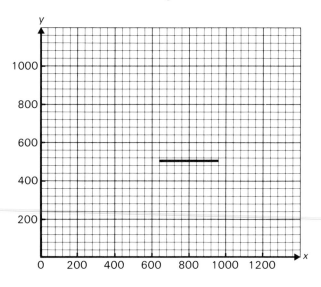

Figure 17

These instructions are written in BASIC, a language which is available on all BBC Micros. In BASIC, a number is needed at the beginning of each line, and the instructions are obeyed in order of the numbers.

EXERCISES

10 Add three more instructions to the list on p. 58 so that the program draws a square on the screen.

11 If possible, check your program by running it on a BBC Micro.

Coordinates in space

Next, we need to be able to describe objects in space, whose pictures are to be created on the computer screen. To do this we also use coordinates, but three values, *X*, *Y* and *Z*, are needed to describe one point. To visualise this, imagine (if necessary!) that you are in a rectangular room: the bottom of the far wall is the *X*-axis, and its left-hand edge is the *Y*-axis. The bottom of the wall on your left provides the *Z*-axis. Think of the units as being metres: your eye could be 2 metres up from the floor, with you standing 4 metres to the right of the left-hand wall and 3 metres in front of the far wall. In this case the coordinates of your eye, in order, would be (4, 2, 3).

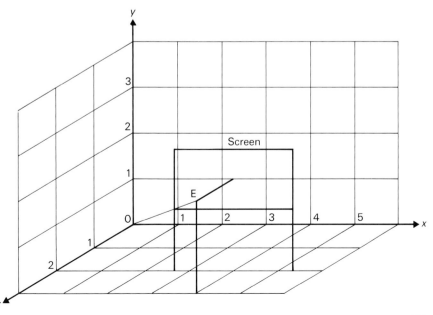

Figure 18

You also need to imagine a computer screen. Think of it as part of a sheet of glass one metre in front of you. (This means where $Z = 2$.) Now stare at the bottom left-hand corner of the far wall. (This is the point $(0, 0, 0)$.) Imagine a mark on the glass where this gaze meets it: this should be the position of the bottom left-hand corner of the computer screen. (Its coordinates can be calculated to be $(\frac{8}{3}, \frac{4}{3}, 2)$.) We will imagine the centre of the computer screen to be directly in front of you on the glass. (This is at $(4, 2, 2)$.) Figure 18, on p. 59, illustrates the situation.

To produce perspective pictures, we go through the now familiar process of joining the points to be represented to the eye, and seeing where this line cuts the glass. The new factor is that this is now done by calculation. If we have a point P in the room at (X, Y, Z), there are formulae which will tell us the coordinates of the point P' representing it on the computer screen. In fact, the formulae are:

$$X' = 4 + \frac{(X - 4)}{(3 - Z)}, \qquad Y' = 2 + \frac{(Y - 2)}{(3 - Z)}, \qquad Z' = 2$$

It is suggested that you take these formulae on trust at the moment. Here X', Y' and Z' are the X, Y, Z coordinates of P'. Notice that Z' is bound to be 2, because P' is a point on the glass sheet. The final stage is to scale these values to fit onto the computer screen. For the BBC Micro we need to multiply by 500, because its screen width is about 1500, while the width of our imaginary screen is 3 units. We also need to allow for the fact that the bottom left-hand corner of our screen has $X = \frac{8}{3}$, $Y = \frac{4}{3}$. This means writing

$$x = 500 \left(X' - \tfrac{8}{3} \right), \qquad y = 500 \left(Y' - \tfrac{4}{3} \right)$$

It will save trouble if we get rid of the X', Y' and Z' which were only a temporary measure. We end up with the point $P(X, Y, Z)$ appearing on the screen at the point $P'(x, y)$ where

$$x = 500 \left[\frac{4}{3} + \frac{(X - 4)}{(3 - Z)} \right] \qquad y = 500 \left[\frac{2}{3} + \frac{(Y - 2)}{(3 - Z)} \right]$$

We are now ready to demonstrate the process in action. Think of the points $A(\frac{7}{2}, 1, 0)$, $B(3, 1, 1)$, $C(4, 1, \frac{3}{2})$ and $D(\frac{9}{2}, 1, \frac{1}{2})$; they form the corners of a horizontal square one metre above the ground with one corner, A, on the back wall. The centre of the square is at $(\frac{15}{4}, 1, \frac{3}{4})$, and so the point $T(\frac{15}{4}, \frac{3}{2}, \frac{3}{4})$ is half a metre above the centre. If we join AB, BC, CD, DA we will get a square; if we also join AT, BT, CT, and DT we will have a pyramid with this square as base.

To produce the picture, first calculate the screen coordinates of the points A', B', C', D' and T' representing A, B, C, D and T. Perhaps you can program a computer to use the formulae just given for this – or you can do the arithmetic yourself. The answers to the nearest whole numbers should be:

A'(583, 166)   B'(416, 83)   C'(666, 0)   D'(766, 133)   T'(611, 222).

Finally, the computer will draw the perspective picture from suitable MOVE and DRAW instructions. A simple but rather clumsy way to do this would be:

```
 10   MODE  4
 20   MOVE  583,166
 30   DRAW  416,83
 40   DRAW  666,0
 50   DRAW  766,133
 60   DRAW  583,166
 70   DRAW  611,222
 80   MOVE  416,83
 90   DRAW  611,222
100   MOVE  666,0
110   DRAW  611,222
120   MOVE  766,133
130   DRAW  611,222
140   END
```

Do try running this program: it should give you a nice picture of a square pyramid!

If you know a bit about programming in BASIC you will be able to write a much neater program to do this. You should also be able to incorporate the calculation stage of the work. An example of a short BASIC program which produces perspective drawings, when you feed in the space coordinates of points together with instructions about which points to join, is given in the Mathematical Association's *132 Short Programs for the Mathematics Classroom* (Stanley Thornes, 1985) p. 91.

EXERCISES

12 Use a computer to draw the pyramid, or, if this is not possible, plot the points yourself on graph paper.

13 Using the points A, B, C, D on p. 60, find the coordinates of another four points E, F, G, and H so that the eight points are vertices of a cube. Work out the coordinates of E', F', G' and H' from the formulae, and plot the cube. (Use a micro for both the calculation and the drawing if possible).

14 Write a BASIC program to make perspective drawings from input data. The data would be the coordinates of the vertices of the figure to be drawn, together with information about which vertices to join.

15 If you know about either enlargements or similar triangles you should be able to prove the formulae used in this section.

Conclusion

This introduction to perspective has been limited in various ways. Essentially it has only been concerned with drawings made up from straight lines. The drawings produced are 'wire-frame' models; to make them look more solid one needs to consider which parts of the frame should be hidden because something else is in front of it. This is easy enough for the human artist, but is quite a difficult problem in computer programming (for a reasonably accessible discussion see I. O. Angell, *A Practical Introduction to Computer Graphics* [Macmillan, 1981]).

On the whole, the focus has been on the practical issue of creating perspective drawings. From a mathematical point of view, the topic is part of Projective Geometry; further developments in this direction are included in W. Wynne Willson, *The Mathematics Curriculum: Geometry* (Blackie, 1977), Chapter 4, and in W. W. Sawyer, *Prelude to Mathematics* (Penguin, 1955), Chapter 10.

A useful further resource on the subject is the video with accompanying booklet *Geometry and Perspective* made by E. C. Zeeman, and available from the Royal Institution (21 Albemarle Street, London W1X 4BS).

Plate 4.1 Courtyard of a House in Delft: Pieter de Hooch (1629–84).
Reproduced by courtesy of the Trustees, the National Gallery, London.

Plate 4.2 Mandolin and Guitar: Pablo Picasso, 1924.
Collection, The Solomon R. Guggenheim Museum, New York;
Photograph by David Heald.
Photograph © 1990 The Solomon
R. Guggenheim Foundation.

Plate 4.3 Christ of St John of the Cross: Salvador Dali,
1951.
Glasgow Art Gallery and Museum.

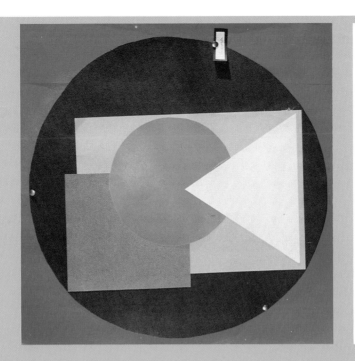

Plate 5.1 and Plate 5.2 Some children coloured in the shapes formed by lines which enclosed them
Photograph   Simon Penberthy

Plate 5.3 The children chose the shape on which to mount their pictures
Photograph   Simon Penberthy

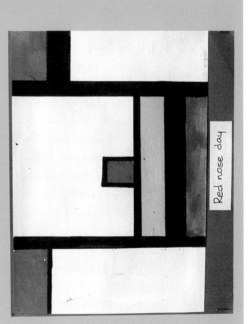

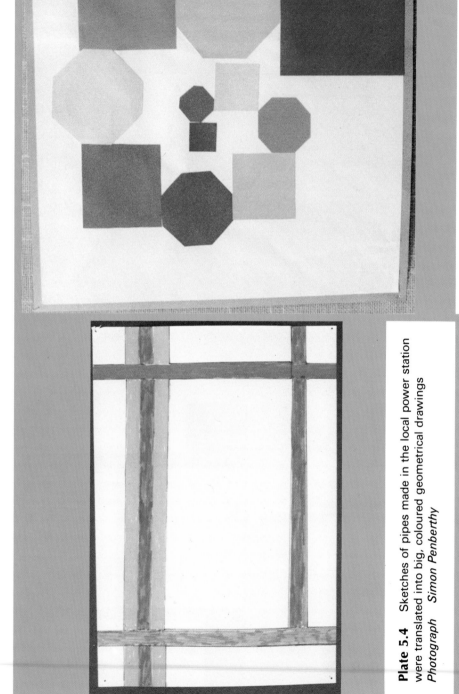

Plate 5.4   Sketches of pipes made in the local power station were translated into big, coloured geometrical drawings
Photograph   Simon Penberthy

Plate 5.5   The children were encouraged to spot and discuss hitherto unnoticed shapes and sequences of shapes
Photograph   Simon Penberthy

Plate 7.1   Detail of a floor in The Red Fort, Lahore, Pakistan
Photograph   Peter Tiller

Plate 8.1   The Mandelbrot Set broods in silent complexity at the centre of a vast two-dimensional plane
Photograph   John Bradshaw

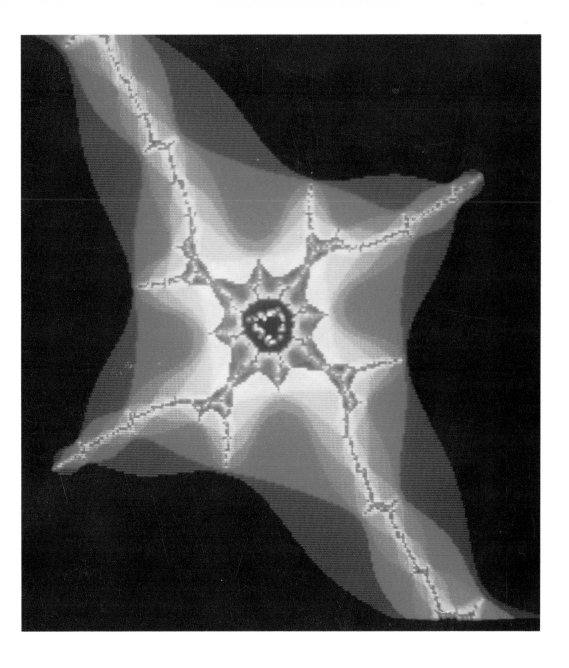

Plate 8.2   The newest and brightest star in the firmament of popular
mathematics
Photograph   John Bradshaw

Plate 8.3 Beauty and Profundity: just one of the infinite number of images
contained within the Mandelbrot Set
Photograph   John Bradshaw

CHAPTER 5 Geometry and Art

5

Jacky Plaster

Initial processes in learning geometry

During my first week in secondary school I was asked to draw a right-angled triangle which, using the sign indicating 90 degrees, innocently I did freehand. This was promptly and rightly returned to me with the instruction to use a ruler and a protractor. Thus, I came to understand that not to use, with attempted precision, a ruler and the other geometrical instruments, was to miss the point of any geometrical drawing at all. Much later, I learnt the usefulness of making an initial free-hand sketch of anything that was to be drawn precisely: that preliminary anticipatory sketches can help to obviate the sort of design problems that crop up in any unwise attempt to complete a drawing in one go. Meanwhile I laboured over very elementary drawing problems. I had been given the goal of getting an accuracy and a refinement in presentation which was germane to the discipline of geometrical drawing and was then left on my own to sort out how to approach it.

I had always enjoyed free-hand drawing, but I had not used geometrical instruments with any forethought. What exercised me first was to rule lines in places where I intended them to go. Stopping any inadvertent shifting of the ruler and angling the finely sharpened pencil against it so that a straight well-placed fine line could be drawn between two finely indicated points, swiftly became a challenging, enjoyable aesthetic activity, a fine art, as did drawing with a consistent pressure of the pencil on the paper, achieving dotted lines with precisely the same interval between each successive dot and drawing carefully measured angles. This enjoyment came despite the low quality of the exercise book paper provided and partly because I already knew that pencil leads were graded from H to B, from hard to soft, providing a range from which I could select the grade appropriate to the task, that is, neither so unresponsive to pressure that it made too thin and faint a mark to be seen easily on the particular paper used, nor so yielding that it produced an over-thick, dark, blurred mark.

I laboured on in lessons which were distributed at intervals throughout that first term, invariably having to put down my ruler and pencil in order to attend to the myriad of other activities that made up the fragmented timetable of the week. I was undeterred, even, by my growing realisation that in geometrical drawing exactitude could never be attained, not even by mechanical printing machines. I saw, for example, that to bisect a right-angle, the bisecting line itself inevitably had a width which, however fine, took up room in space, thus necessitating the use of some device, like the writing of the figures 45 in each angle, to indicate their identicality. I concluded that however skilfully executed, geometrical drawing was nothing but a concrete representation, a necessarily imprecise graphic device used to illustrate a feature of an abstract, coherent conceptual system in which imprecision had no part to play. I could not have put this conclusion easily into words then, but I understood it, and would have progressed faster had the drawing side of geometric representation been discussed in class. Then, I could have talked myself through difficulties and in conversation I could have become more fluent and articulate about what I was trying to do and what I was trying to understand.

As I was captivated by the activity of geometrical drawing, it became of paramount importance to me to get these representations looking 'right'. How otherwise could the ideas to which they referred be made intelligible to the viewer? To draw a right-angle, for example, looking even slightly less, or slightly more, than 90 degrees clearly was to deny its salient, ascribed geometric characteristic.

Of course things, simple things, sometimes went wrong. Lines inadvertently over-shot, travelling to unintended places, thus, for example, little crosses, like minute horns, appeared at the corners of triangles. Rubbing them out and repairing the apex tended to leave an unpleasant grey roughed-up surface on the paper. Erasure which removed only that which was unwanted also became a fine art. When one line in a triangle was thicker than the other two, it had to be rubbed out delicately and the pencil carefully re-sharpened, before it was drawn in again to look, as far as possible, correct. When the lead in a pencil was even slightly too hard, or pressure on the pencil too great, old rubbed-out lines made visible indentations in the paper and too much rubbing-out with hard rubbers damaged paper surfaces irremediably. Moments of despair were occasioned by using rulers, protractors and hands grey with faint, unnoticed films of graphite pencil dust, some of which, despite efforts to blow it off the paper, in the act of drawing clung to and smeared hitherto pristine drawings.

Design problems also arose. One was precisely where to place a geometrical drawing on the blank page of a school exercise book so that it looked well: not crooked, not crammed against the edge and not off-centre. Another consideration was how big to make the drawing in relation to the size of the page. A drawing can appear lost in a vast space, uncomfortably pressed into an insufficient one, and, most dispiriting of all, can fail to fit on the page in its entirety thus necessitating very much rubbing out indeed, or, at worst, the removal of pages from, what became in my case, a rapidly-thinning exercise book.

A major graphic-design problem was writing out letters, numbers, titles and, later on, theorems in hand-writing and placing these aesthetically in relation to the drawings. My hand-writing spoiled the look of the pages because I was too inconsistent in the formation of individual letters for it to look really smart.

For example, sometimes I wrote an 'l' with a loop and sometimes not; the joining-up of the individual letters looked either uncertain or over-emphasised, never entirely regularly connected; letters and words did not lean consistently either to the left or to the right; the overall size of my script, with all its faults, varied from day to day and its horizontal orientation on the page invariably was erratic.

Although I did not solve any of these design problems of systematising layout, certainly I became aware of them. I looked at how other people approached them. I looked at the way books, newspapers and film credits were set out. Concentration on the means of graphic representation had required persistence, visual acuity and skills in handling geometrical instruments. In asking myself if a drawing worked, I knew that I could make alterations to improve the look and the clarity of what I was putting down. In so doing I understood that people made up both graphic and mathematical systems through which they intended and attempted to communicate.

None of this consoled me. I was dissatisfied with the appearance of my geometry book. I had wanted to produce one that was immaculate, not the flawed book I had so laboriously filled. I desired the reward of an immaculate book because I had not yet learned to identify and to value fully the on-going experiences and interim products of learning, only the final, visible and, ideally, perfect end-product of continuous effort. Looking back, how could I have done better?

Geometry and art

In 1915, a Russian artist, Kasimir Malevich, had proclaimed the advent of a new fine art movement which was called *Suprematism*, in which pure geometric shapes were used in various combinations by the artists in both two- and three-dimensional work. Had I known this when I was filling my benighted exercise book, I could have extended the scope of my schoolwork in many directions, but the knowledge was not available to school children in 1945 as it is today.

Malevich was one of three Russian artists who initiated a period of intense and extensive experimentation by artists in Russia, Eastern Europe, Central Europe and the West. In 1915 he exhibited a painting called *The Black Quadrilateral*, featuring a black square placed on a white ground. This quadrilateral was not tilted away from the picture plane, but faced the spectator in an uncompromising centrality of position within its white margins. It was an unambiguous statement of defiance and of innovation in which he abandoned the concerns of all those who in their art strove to portray, mirror or refer to living creatures, artefacts or natural objects in the world. He saw pure, non-objective art as superseding the contemporary modern movements in European art, including those of Cubism and Futurism; hence the name given to the new movement, Suprematism.

Working at the same time at Malevich in 1913, a Russian sculptor, Vladimir Tatlin, who was deeply interested in the qualities and the potential use of materials, started to make non-figurative reliefs, from which he progressed to experimenting with fully three-dimensional shapes. His innovatory, non-objective constructions, like Malevich's paintings, were based on purely geometric forms. The third Russian artist to invent non-objective art was the painter Olga Rosanova, who died prematurely. A member of Malevich's Supremus group and very sensitive, like Tatlin, to the texture of materials, she used colour in highly original ways to weight the forms and to create the dynamic space of her innovative collages and paintings.

These artists used very forcible language to express their rejection of what they saw as out-moded art forms. Malevich spoke of their renouncing of the old servitudes of the narrative element of painting, of realism in the portrayal of objects and of the prettiness of composition. By contrast, the new geometric art was experienced as liberating, pure and dynamic, in other words, as supreme in its non-objectivity. Malevich called his *Black Quadrilateral*, 'a majestic new-born' and 'a royal infant': descriptions which indicate to me the powerful emotions invested by him in the creation of the new non-objective art.

Until 1919 the term 'suprematism' and 'non-objectivism' were used interchangeably. In that year an exhibition entitled, 'Non-objective Creation and Suprematism', was held in Moscow to commemorate the art of Olga Rosanova, who had died the year before. During this exhibition most of the non-objective artists dissociated themselves from Malevich's most recent work and also from his latest theoretical position on the function of the artist. In his account of the Russian avante-garde, the art historian, Andrei Nakov, describes how, until 1917, Malevich had created 'suprematist' planes in his paintings which were achieved by a wealth of geometric forms placed to construct, in the artist's own words, a dynamic of 'speed, weight and direction of movement'. (Nakov, 1986).

Malevich's next development was to begin to abandon precision by dissolving the edges of what were, by now, the very few planes in his paintings. Increasingly, the formal exactitude required by geometric delineation is replaced by an exploration of an amorphous, inchoate space in which the planes no longer are orchestrated tautly and dynamically in relation to each other, but are softly incorporeal. Some subsequent paintings contain only a part of one plane, whose total shape, and whose direction of movement in space, are virtually impossible to ascertain. After these he painted his series of white-on-white paintings, which includes one of a white square, diagonally tilted on the picture plane and lightly drawn on an evanescent white ground.

The deliberately-sought ambiguity within all these paintings is a result of his conviction that artists should be free to develop their art, that is, they should not be constrained by any static rules of acceptable practice, not even by their own ideals which had fired them in the past, but that new ideas should be followed through to wherever they might lead. His own pursuance of the dissolution of geometric boundaries and his shift away from the juxtaposition of colours to his white paintings, led him to proclaim in 1920 that paintings had long been obsolete and that the painter was a 'prejudice from the past'! The character of the developments in his work, towards the exploration of ambiguity and therefore away from the clear delineation of geometric form, his philosophical idealism and his disconcerting conclusion, all impelled the dissenting non-objective painters to find their own course.

At first, in reaction to Malevich's shift away from non-objectivism, they re-asserted, simplified and tightened up their own articulation of geometric form in order to be certain to eliminate what they felt were irrelevant and unwanted metaphysical features and approaches. This helped them to take their next step towards designing utilitarian art. They became known as the Russian Constructivists, a group diametrically opposed to the enquiring, philosophical idealism of the remaining Suprematists.

By 1921 several Constructivists also had renounced painting, but for a reason that was entirely unacceptable to the idealist philosophers of Suprematism. Exploration of pure form for its own sake, these Constructivists argued, had no social utility. Thus they came finally to reject their previously held notion of an autonomous, non-objective art. In their last analysis they saw it as misguidedly and irresponsibly utopian. In an interim period, however, they had conceived non-objectivist art somewhat differently as a necessary, preliminary, scientific investigation of new forms, materials and processes. This they had seen as leading to the new knowledge urgently needed for application and development within the technology of industrial production in communist Russia.

Vladimir Tatlin became a Constructivist, as did his former pupil, a younger man called Alexander Rodchenko, who in 1921 exhibited abstract drawings he had chosen to produce with geometrical instruments rather than drawing them freehand. This was in order to obviate any ambiguity of line resulting from what he saw as the inevitable, and, for him, the wholly undesirable imprecisions of freehand drawing. He wanted a technical, some would say a technicist, perfection in the execution and outcome of drawing. Constructivist artists in Russia went on to become directly involved in the design and production of material goods and also of political propaganda. They saw themselves as materialists, as artist-engineers, as technicians of industrial production who were fully and usefully participant in the life of their society, that is, not hived off into the ivory tower of the idealists.

In the early years of the Communist Revolution, of the civil war, and in the ensuing decades, Russian artists experienced many vicissitudes. Fine art research and teaching programmes were state-funded for a time and then suspended. Finally, as Nakov reports, in 1932 independent art organisations were disallowed and in 1934 Stalin's government decreed that there should be only one, homogeneous, permitted style of art, that of Social Realism (Nakov, 1986). By this time, many of Russia's artists had emigrated. Others stayed to work within the constraints of the law.

Geometric art in the classroom

Recently I supervised the teaching practice of a student who worked with a fourth-year class of primary children. He interested them in making their own geometrically-based art. From the college library they were given well-produced, well-illustrated books about Suprematist and Constructivist art and design, to consult and to browse through. He set them carefully worked-out, specific guide-lines within which they were asked to invent their own geometric designs. In very practical ways they were introduced to two of the most significant art movements of this century.

What began as a means of linking geometry and art in the classroom concluded with the children having built on the understanding of their own environment. However vestigially, they began to appreciate that their immediate world, which they looked at every day, had been influenced by the decisions of many women and men, including those of artists and designers, working over half a century before they were born. They only needed to take a further step to ask who else, as well as the non-objectivists, had been similarly influential.

The student started them off making geometric shapes, which, as he expected, required a lot of organisation and explanation as the children tried to establish just what they were required to do and what was acceptable. It was only when, with a pair of primary school scissors, I tried to cut out from a square of paper my institution's circular parking disc in order to put it in a plastic holder on my windscreen, that I realised fully what level of skills was being required of these ten-year-olds. My disc, like some of theirs, got smaller and smaller as I tried to cut out a precise circle. Finally, in order to avoid applying for another one I had to accept the imperfections. Inadvertently I had cut the curved line straight in places. It looked what it was, ineptly cut out.

Experiences like these can sensitise us to the achievements of others. We can scrutinise the drawing of halos, for example, in paintings in the National Gallery to see if their curves are immaculately drawn. We simply do not expect them to be faulty. Scrutiny of just this one feature of such religious paintings can be full of surprises, particularly if we have been trying to draw our own ellipses, and it can lead to sometimes disconcerting discoveries. Similarly with modern geometric drawing, we expect it to look right and to be right, and we can be disconcerted by that which our close scrutiny sometimes reveals.

These sorts of things were talked through with the children. A useful example of a painting which could be discussed with children is in Camilla Gray's book, *The Great Experiment: Russian Art 1863-1922*, a reproduction of Kasimir Malevich's work in greys, creams, yellows and black, called *Dynamic Suprematism* (1916). There is a circular shape in it that is not completely round and another curve that is not entirely smooth. Yet, although these curves are straight in places, they do not look 'wrong' to me.

We all know that some imprecisions are the result of ineptitude, or a lack of instruction, a lack of practice with tools, a lack of useful equipment in the classroom, workshop or studio (like cutting mats, for example), or merely uncorrected mistakes left for whatever reason. Importantly though, we need to hold in mind that the deliberate use of imprecision can be a very interesting and necessary device. If an artist never breaks the rules of precision which he or she has decided to follow, a deadening mechanical appearance, or other unintended visual consequences, can result. Sometimes, a line actually has to be bowed in order for it to look straight. The ancient Greeks, for example, made the column shafts in their temples slightly convex in order to correct the optical illusion of concavity.

We have seen, however, that the non-objective artists wanted their art to be free of any ambiguity. Ambiguity they saw as a device of composition in the old art, not as a tool of construction in the new. Equally, too, it can be argued, as Rodchenko did, that the objective of complete precision actually can promote invention.

How can a lapse from the pure form of objective art be identified? Looking to see if the straight lines in *Dynamic Suprematism* really were straight, which they were, I noticed how the overlaying of smaller geometrical shapes on the large grey triangular one created many more triangular shapes than I had previously seen, their placing contributing to the contrapuntal diagonal rhythms of the painting. Thus, looking at one feature brought another to my attention. In so doing I experienced what I felt to be a disconcerting non-objective ambiguity in the design. In many cases the third sides of small triangles had not been drawn in by the artist, but, in following the diagonal directions in which the two main axes pointed, they could be imagined by the spectator. Thus they were, and at the same time they were not, completed. This could have been because actually to have drawn in every possible line would have made the drawing too full and impacted and thus would have slowed down the rhythms which created the dynamic dimension. Possibly this is an example of impurity in his design, a device of composition rather than of construction. We know that, as his ideas developed, Malevitch was to be disowned by many of the other non-objective painters for allowing overt ambiguities, which they regarded as mystifying and effete, to feature in his paintings.

In discussing this particular painting with children, they could be asked if they could spot hidden or implied shapes and whether or not they thought that all the triangles should have been drawn in completely. They could be asked to put themselves in the place of the artist. Without expressing his/her own preference or opinion, the teacher could emphasise that changing one's mind is alright, as much as not always being sure of what one would have done. Depending on the circumstances, children could be encouraged to take up partisan stances in conversation, which they could add to, modify, or, if they wanted, go on to reject. They could be encouraged to be analytical and speculative, in small doses, as it were, and gently, in order to build up their confidence and to give them time to reflect. Rather than attempting to achieve this with the whole class at the same time, the teacher could rely on his/her conversations with individuals and with groups being overheard, to a certain extent, by the rest. Even while doing other things the rest of the children could consider what was being asserted, questioned and suggested, before their own turn came to talk through their ideas.

As I have not seen *Dynamic Suprematism* in the Tretyakov Gallery in Moscow, I do not know how it looks in the original at the distance from which the artist intended that it should be viewed. Valuable though it can be, a small reproduction can distort the impact of a work of art and can reduce the amount of information available to the viewer. Fortunately, towards the end of the practice, the student, his class teacher and the class were able to go from their primary school in south-east London to visit The Crafts Council Gallery in Waterloo Place to see the University of East Anglia Collection of non-objective, constructive, art movements in this century and the related fields of architecture and design.

They had each made their own geometric designs back at school and had pinned them up on every available wall and cupboard space in their classroom (see Figure 1).

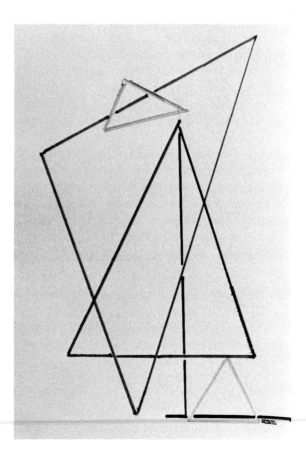

Figure 1   Each child made a geometric design

Having sketched, measured, drawn, re-drawn, cut out, overlaid, juxtaposed, repeated, shadowed, arranged and re-arranged geometrical shapes in many different materials over several weeks, and having read and talked about what they were doing and discussed aspects of the books that they had looked at, they were able to scrutinise with empathy and to pay critical attention to the exhibition, which included originals of some of the work that they had seen in reproduction. Using clip-boards, pencils and paper they drew from any drawing, print, painting, design, three-dimensional construction or artefact that interested them.

Back at school some worked from their rough sketches and drew their own version of an original they had sketched. An example is shown in Figure 2. Some of the children could have taken their interest further on their own initiative. They each went back to school, I believe, with an increased understanding of the lives of the artists and designers whose work they had studied. The basis for a further, historical understanding of some of the art and design issues of their own time had been laid.

Figure 2   A reinterpretation of a drawing by Lazlo Moholy Nagy

To start the project the class had been divided into three groups. One went into the playground to make sketches of the familiar, solid, worn school gate and of teachers' cars parked in the road outside. When they returned to the classroom they used geometrical instruments to 'geometricise' their sketches. Gradually they got the idea. They each chose the scale of their new drawings. Some were very small and precise. Most reduced their sketches of the school gate completely to non-objective lines and quadrilaterals, with a few focusing on details of the gate handle. They had not been told to get rid of the object, some just chose to. All those who sketched cars kept them (the object) intact, that is, they were instantly recognisable as cars, even though the descriptive, sometimes wobbly lines of their sketches had been re-drawn as taut geometric shapes. Most of these children voluntarily had three or four attempts before they were satisfied with their final geometric forms. They were encouraged to value each drawing and to display them in the sequence in which they had been drawn, so that they could see the progression of their ideas (see Figure 3).

Figure 3   The children redrew their sketches as taut geometric shapes

Another group was asked to build up geometric designs using lines of varying thicknesses, so that the thicker ones actually looked like blocked-in rectangles rather than lines. This was deliberate in order that they should think about whether it is possible to distinguish between a straight line and a rectangle. Each line had to be colour-coded so that it was instantly obvious which were, for example, one centimetre thick, because they were coloured in blue; or, for example, exceptionally fine, because they were coloured in red. A voluntary development was that sometimes geometric shapes enclosed by lines, themselves became coloured in (see Plates 5.1 and 5.2). Another development was that the initial rectangular shape of the paper became trimmed down to, for example, a big triangle or a big circle in which other geometric shapes had been placed (see Plate 5.3).

A third group worked on cutting out geometric shapes from one piece of paper which they overlaid on another sheet of a different colour. At first this group was envied as having what appeared to be the easiest and most interesting task, but their difficulties were soon appreciated as they struggled to cut out with school scissors and without cutting mats. Geometric forms had to be modified as mistakes were made. Again, voluntarily, the initial rectangles sometimes were trimmed down to other basic geometric shapes.

A few children who either were stuck, or who had floated around the groups, were directed by the class teacher to use the overhead projector where they became absorbed in making illuminated, transparent, coloured geometric shapes. Some of their transparencies were entirely non-objective, others developed towards geometricised representations of objects like, for example, a dog.

In the middle of his teaching practice the student went with the class on a visit to a power station. This visit was intended as part of a separate project of the class teacher, unconnected with the student's own. Both of them were surprised and very pleased when, entirely unprompted, several children drew sketches of tiers of horizontal pipes they saw there, which, back at school, they translated into big, coloured geometricised drawings (see Plate 5.4). A selection was taken to the college and displayed there after the student's practice, and the children went to see the exhibition. They discussed with the mathematics lecturers the geometric dimensions of their work and they were encouraged to spot hitherto un-noticed shapes and sequences of shapes, such as spirals (see Plate 5.5).

Thinking mathematically

The geometry and art project had much potential for opening out into a fuller cultural understanding, whilst at the same time ensuring specifically that children, at very least, could 'estimate, measure and record lengths using suitable standard units', could 'know when a line is bent or moved its length stays the same', could 'carry out practical activities which need calculations

73

with length', had 'memorised the common units of length' and could 'solve written problems about length'. The ten-year-old children could fulfil these assessment criteria and further ones involved in the construction of a variety of geometrical shapes of widely varying scale.

In a future project of this kind, attainment targets referring to the desired levels of achievement will have to be carefully inserted into the project design and held in mind for the day-to-day planning, but this need not interefere with the freedom of children to make their own choices and decisions within an enabling framework that has been structured by a teaching team or by individual teachers. Children given such freedom can contribute to discussion of the best ways to plan and to proceed with projects, and thereby can gain understanding of cooperatively devised strategies for learning.

In the National Curriculum document on Design and Technology (DES, 1989), the single profile component, Design and Technological Capability, is broken down into four attainment targets: Identifying needs and opportunities; Generating a design proposal; Planning and making; Appraising. The various processes involved in these are not 'undertaken in sequential isolation, but interact and feed into each other continuously'. Each target is linked to ten levels of achievement.

Clearly a linear approach to the teaching of skills and of concepts is not advocated, but rather a holistic one in which the individual is to be pro-active, analytical and critical. The geometry and art project could have been orientated to the use of design and technology materials and skills, which would have been appropriate given the ideological debates concerning technological innovation that raged in the historical period which they studied, and, given that the development of design and technology was deeply influenced by the Constructivist design concepts.

Utopian visions and geometric art

In April 1989, two drawings of the Russian revolutionary artist, Alexander Rodchenko, were sold at Sotheby's in London, an event amongst others that confirms that there is an ongoing renewed interest in, and re-evaluation of, Constructivism. Constructivism, the movement in modern art which followed Cubism and Futurism in the early twenties in Russia, Eastern and Central Europe and the West, was infused with utopian ideals, but the different groups of Constructivist artists did not share identical utopian visions. Often their differences were fundamental. Richard Stites (1989), writes about the utopian visions prevalent in the early years of the Russian revolution, when hopes of radical change were high. One vision was of communities of equals within newly built, radically designed housing estates, in which the lives of all, but particularly of women, would be freed from servitudes like that of housework. Some designers and architects dreamed of new linear towns stretching for hundreds of miles across Russia. Others dreamed of gigantic bridges linking new mega-cities in North America with their counterparts in Siberia. Geometry mediated between the various utopias and reality.

Esther Levinger (1987) writes about Constructivist art in Hungary after the fall of the Hungarian Soviet Republic in 1919. She cites the painter Lajos Kassak and the critic Ernst Kallai's theory of a trinity of technology, art and communism, and follows their complex arguments from which they concluded that, although the art of communism had to be Constructivism, neither of them were ends in themselves, only the means for further change, therefore both eventually would be superseded.

In his black and white lino-cuts, for their journal, *Today* (colour was too expensive), and later in his wood engravings, Kassak used simple, clear, non-objective geometric forms similar to those in the work of the Russian Constructivists, but there was no sharing of a body of similar ideas. As a socialist himself, Kassak made it clear to the Russians that he did not support their Proletkult (Proletarian Cultural and Educational Organisations). He did not believe in either a proletarian mathematics or in a proletarian art. For Kassak art was revolutionary, but not utilitarian. He abhorred any denial of aesthetics. He praised the Russian Constructivists for refusing to allow that art should be the servant of politics, and criticised them for becoming entrapped by what he called 'the romanticism of technology'. He believed that the basic structure of the universe was geometric and that therefore art had to be geometric.

Kallai saw Constructivist art as being dialectically connected with modern technological structures, materials and production methods. He thought that, in what should be a mutally stimulating exchange of ideas, artists always were on a higher level than technologists, due to the superior energy that he believed went into the making of art, over and above the necessary intellectual clarity, and mathematical and technical precision that they shared with technologists!

Kassak and Kallai certainly did not interpret the term 'Constructivism' as indicating that the artists inevitably would be subsumed into industrial production as artist-engineers, or as makers of utilitarian objects. They did not, as did their Russian contemporaries, see technology as the art of the new communist economic system. They believed that a clear and harmonious constructivist geometrical system would reflect an equally clear and harmonious system of human relations, with communism being the liberating means: that constructivism, in its drive to solve formal problems, was the paradigm of a communist ethic. However, they also strongly held a notion of permanent revolution. Communism and Constructivism inevitably were only to be stages in a continuous forward dynamic of development and change. They could not, and should not be clung on to because they would become archaic and obsolete. The first of their trinity, technology, too, inevitably, would change.

From a book of articles edited by Hilary Gresty and Jeremy Lewison (1983) we learn that Wladyslaw Strzeminski and Katarzyna Kobro, Constructivists in Poland, engaged in a process of analysing and reformulating the principles of art, using their new understanding in their revolutionary projects in architecture, urban and industrial design, typography and mass theatre. By 1924 they regarded the progressive laboratory research into new form as something that should precede and influence the deployment of technology, and felt that artists should not be subject to, or marginalised by, any utilitarian imperatives governing industrial production.

They, and Kassak and Kallai in Hungary, according to Levinger, were the only Constructivists to reject the idea of an absolute Constructivist form: they believed that artists would develop and change the forms of their art, that art would continue to have a history and not be stilled within any social utopia. They implemented a new system of art education in which artistic principles were learnt separately before being synthesised into what they called 'creative production'. They became interested in architecture as a process of continual renewal. Strzeminski introduced the concept of 'functionalist type' and in his layout for avant-garde Polish poets he tried to achieve a visual poetry. Kobro achieved control over contemporary industrial processes, using her knowledge of them in her sculpture to achieve pure synethetic systems. She believed strongly that development in art through systematic experimentation should not be undermined by the pressure of the possibility of any immediate translation into mass production.

Strzeminski and Kobro worked together to fuse their individual artistic concepts in a theory, 'The Composition of Space', in which Strzeminski accepted Kobro's view on the unity between nature and spatial construction. In his architectural compositions he relied on 'a uniform system of mathematical calculations'. They agreed that spatial constructions satisfy all conditions devised for mathematically calculated work.

In the twenties and thirties the Polish Constructivists were members of international groups, participated in international exhibitions and published their writing and reproduced their art in foreign art magazines.

Contemporary interest in geometric art

In our own turbulent, changing environment, with the development of computer technology, with new forms of economic and political alliance within the European Community, with popular uprisings against Stalinist forms of communism in Central and Eastern Europe, as well as in the USSR, and with the insertion of the notions of glasnost and perestroika into political debate, I suggest that we need to identify certain key concepts to introduce to children, in order to help them to map their own way through the knowledge they will need in order to make sense of their world in the future. Included amongst these concepts could be those of the artist-engineer, of utopian visions of the future and of perpetual social and technological change.

Tessellations and the Work of M. C. Escher

Lesley Jones

M. C. Escher

The relationship between mathematics and art is seen very clearly in the work of the Dutch artist Maurits Escher (1898–1972). Escher expressed his own doubts about the status of his work as art or mathematics, though he certainly did not regard himself as a mathematician. His experience at school had generally been very unhappy. Art was the only subject at which he shone and even here his final examination results were disappointing.

When he left school it was decided that he should train as an architect, so in 1919 he went to study at the school of Architecture and Decorative Arts in Haarlem. Early in the course it became clear that his talent lay in the field of graphic art, so the architecture course was abandoned and Escher started to concentrate on the woodcut. Even in this field his talents were not regarded as outstanding. His work was seen as lacking expression; he interpreted things literally and methodically. According to his official college report he was '. . . too tight, too literary-philosophical, a young man too lacking in feeling or caprice, too little of an artist' (Ernst, 1985, p. 7). He left the school in 1922 after two years of study. During these two years he had already made some explorations into regular divisions of the plane and was fascinated by the possibility of creating patterns which fitted together to cover a plane surface completely. Generally he used either congruent shapes or a group of similar shapes, so that a regular pattern was formed (see Figure 1, p. 78).

In 1936 Escher visited the Alhambra in Spain and was completely entranced by the complex patterns used by the Moors to cover the surfaces. He and his wife sat for days making sketches of the patterns and tessellations. From these he built up his own ideas about the motifs and movements which would allow him to cover the plane. He seemed to regret the restrictions of the Islamic tradition which meant that the patterns did not contain images. The development of his strange, but recognisable creatures was a feature which clearly added much enjoyment to Escher's work.

He wrote:

> What a pity it was that Islam forbade the making of 'Images'. In their tessellations they restricted themselves to figures with abstracted geometrical shapes. So far as I know, no single Moorish artist ever made so bold (or maybe the idea never dawned on him) as to use concrete, recognisable figures such as birds, fish, reptiles and

human beings as elements of their tessellations. Then I find this restriction all the more unacceptable because it is the recognisability of the components of my own patterns that is the reason for my never-ceasing interest in this domain.

Escher in Ernst, 1985, p. 37

Figure 1   Eight heads
Collection Haags Gemeentemuseum – The Hague

An isometry is the term used for a movement which retains the shape and size of the original motif. The isometries which can be used and combined to cover the plane are translation (a move in one direction), reflection (a mirror image), rotation (a movement about a point) and glide reflection (a movement which combines a reflection with a translation). Using these, it is possible to find seventeen different pattern structures. Escher found all of these patterns in the course of his work. For someone without a mathematical background this in itself is remarkable. His explorations of limits and hyperbolic geometry in work such as *Circle Limit III* give evidence of a tremendous ability in mathematics and understanding of its laws, even though this was not 'formalised' knowledge. At the time when he was working on the theme of infinity he was in correspondence with the mathematician Professor H. S. M. Coxeter. His print, *Circle Limit I* is very closely modelled on an illustration by Coxeter of the principles of hyperbolic geometry.

It would be a mistake to interpret the mathematics Escher used as being limited to the essentially practical and pragmatic level. Whilst he refers to his own layman's theory, his ideas gradually gained in sophistication so that the methods became easier for him. He started working on the regular division of the plane without any knowledge of the ground rules. So much of his work was involved in 'doing' mathematics in a creative way. What he was not able to do was to express his ideas in the formal language of the trained mathematician.

Escher was well aware that he was working in a new way and against the mainstream of contemporary thought.

> How slowly one moves in a boat that is not floating with the current. How much easier it is to continue the work of illustrious predecessors whose worth is accepted by everyone. A personal experiment, an edifice where one has to dig the foundations and build the walls oneself stands a good chance of turning into a ramshackle shed, and yet one may choose to live there rather than a palace built by somone else.
>
> Escher in Locher, 1982, p. 164

In an essay written about his hobby, the regular division of the plane, Escher uses powerful imagery to describe his route through mathematical and artistic exploration. He refers to a high wall and his premonition that there was something hidden behind it. After a difficult climb he landed on the other side and had to struggle through a wilderness until he found the open gate of mathematics.

> I walk around all alone in this beautiful garden, which certainly does not belong only to me, but whose gate is open to everyone. I feel a revitalising yet oppressive sense of loneliness.
>
> Escher in Locher, 1982, p. 156

He was a quiet, rather private person, but his sense of humour comes through in his writing and in his graphic works. His interest in 2D and 3D representation seems sometimes to be poking fun at the form he uses. In one of my favourite lithographs *Reptiles*, Figure 2 on p. 80, he allows the creatures to climb right out of the drawings and appear to become fully fledged 3D creatures, clambering over mathematical instruments and learned tomes before returning to the page of his book. Yet the whole thing takes place in two dimensions. In his famous series of impossible figures he makes a joke of representing, in 2D, buildings which could not exist in reality yet which are hard to fault as they appear in the plane.

By making connections in school between different subject areas, we may be able to open gates to children and allow their appreciation of one discipline to help them to enjoy another. Mathematics has a poor reputation in terms of enjoyability. Yet with Escher's work we see how it can become an absorbing pastime and the bedrock of one form of artistic expression.

Figure 2   Reptiles
© 1989 M. C. Escher Heirs/Cordon Art – Baarn – Holland
Collection Haags Gemeentemuseum – The Hague

None of the suggestions for work in the classroom are revolutionary, but I would hope they provide a progression of ideas which link together and enable art and mathematics to be developed alongside each other. They are not aimed at a specific age range. Many of the ideas can be used throughout the years of schooling and developed to the appropriate level. Spatial aspects of mathematics seem to have this quality to a far greater extent than numerical aspects. I am constantly surprised by college students who will work at a problem at their own level, fully engaged with it and then find a way to present the same problem to very young children, so that they, too become fully engaged with it. This is an example of Bruner's notion of the 'spiral curriculum', in which concepts can be revisited at intervals, but can always be presented to a learner in an appropriate form (Bruner, 1960).

Art in the mathematics room

The term 'tessellation' literally means a tiling. The mathematician is interested in ways in which shapes can tile together leaving no gaps. (This is considered in the ideal situation, that is to say, cement and grouting are disregarded. One might note that a bathroom contractor has a different view of ideal from that of a mathematician!) A *regular tessellation* is one composed of identical regular polygons. To be regular, a polygon must have all sides and angles equal.

The number of regular polygonal tessellations is very limited. Experimentation with tiles such as the ATM *Mats*[1] will soon reveal that only the equilateral triangle, the square and the hexagon will form tessellations on their own. This can be 'proved' by checking through the list of possible shapes. For three-sided shapes the equilateral triangle is the only possible regular tile (see Figure 3a). The tiling shows six shapes meeting at each point. If we consider four-sided shapes the square is the only one which has equal angles and sides. Four shapes meet at each point (see Figure 3b). A regular pentagon leaves a gap (see Figure 3c). A regular hexagon tessellates, with 3 shapes meeting at each point (see Figure 3d).

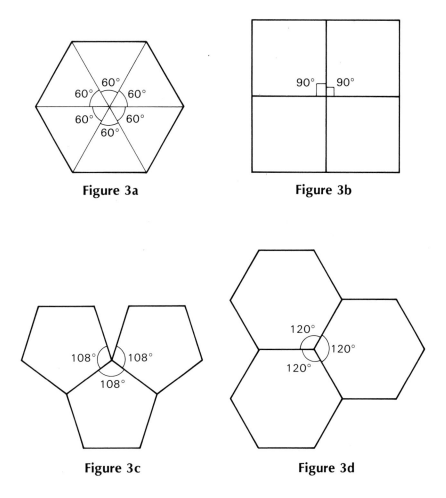

Figure 3a   **Figure 3b**

Figure 3c   **Figure 3d**

[1]ATM *Mats* are available from Association of Teachers of Mathematics, 7 Shaftesbury St, Derby DE3 8BY

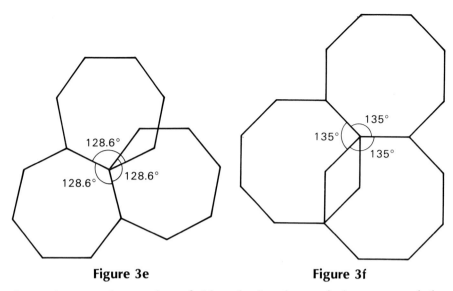

Figure 3e   **Figure 3f**

As we increase the number of sides, the interior angle increases and the number of shapes which meet at a point decreases. Since the hexagon has three shapes which meet at a point we would expect any other polygon to meet with less than three shapes at a node, but this would be impossible. Two shapes cannot meet at a point, they can only meet to form a straight line. Some experimentation with octagonal, decagonal tiles, etc. will enable children to verify this for themselves.

Semi-regular tessellations

When two or more *different* regular polygons are fitted together they make a *semi-regular tessellation* provided that each node is identical. The tessellation is named according to the number of sides of the shapes which meet at a node. So (3. 3. 4. 3. 4) describes the tessellation in Figure 4. The convention is to begin naming with the lowest numbers.

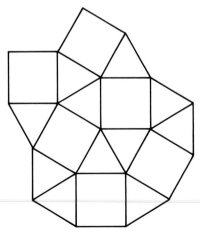

Figure 4   (3.3.4.3.4)

There are only eight semi-regular tessellations. Some of these are used as basic grids for the Islamic patterns which Escher so admired. Using mats or tiles which have sides of equal length children can discover these patterns for themselves (see Figures 5 to 11).

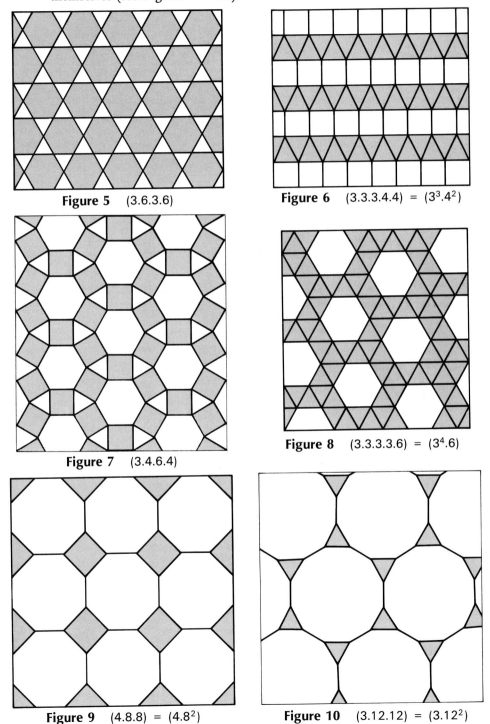

Figure 5   (3.6.3.6)

Figure 6   (3.3.3.4.4) = ($3^3.4^2$)

Figure 7   (3.4.6.4)

Figure 8   (3.3.3.3.6) = ($3^4.6$)

Figure 9   (4.8.8) = (4.8^2)

Figure 10   (3.12.12) = (3.12^2)

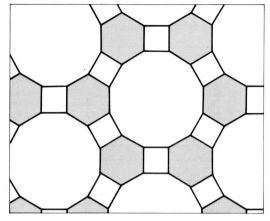

Figure 11   (4.6.12)

A different way to approach the same problem would be to set the following investigation.

How many different ways are there for a combination of these shapes to meet at a point?

- equilateral triangle
- square
- regular pentagon
- regular hexagon
- regular heptagon
- regular octagon
- regular nonagon
- regular decagon
- regular hendecagon
- regular dodecagon

With the knowledge that there are 360° at a point the problem could be approached purely numerically. In my view, it is when the two approaches are combined that the real understanding takes place; when the spatial and practical activities are linked with the theoretical exercises.

Non-regular tessellations

Many polygons can be arranged in such a way that they form a tessellation. All triangles will tessellate and all quadrilaterals will tessellate. We can see that this is so by examining their interior angles (see Figure 12).

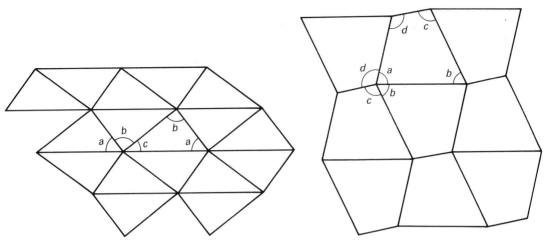

Figure 12a $a + b + c = 180°$ **Figure 12b** $a + b + c + d = 360°$

EXERCISES

1 Use a set of regular polygons to find all of the possible regular tessellations.

When you are sure you have found them all write a few lines to explain why there cannot be any more.

2 Use a set of regular polygons to find some semi-regular tessellations. Remember that the combination and order of polygons meeting at any point must be identical. Keep a record of those that you find.

3 Make a template of an irregular triangle and quadrilateral. Use each separately to create a tessellation.

Compare your findings with other pupils'. Did each triangle tessellate? Did each quadrilateral tessellate?

Isometries in the plane

All repeating patterns such as those found in wallpaper and fabrics are based on a parallelogram lattice or grid. These may differ to the extent that the grid is composed of squares, rectangles or rhombuses (each of which is a special case of the parallelogram), but essentially the structure will be based on a parallelogram grid. Within each pattern we can find the basic motif or tile and consider how it has been moved to cover the plane. Each pattern will have its own rule. In discussing this it is helpful to imagine a very thin transparent lamina (such as a large thin glass sheet) covering the patterned surface. On the sheet imagine you have drawn the bare bones of the pattern we are considering. We can then slide the sheet from one section of the pattern to another to see if it repeats in an identical way. In tessellating patterns there are four isometries which are likely to be used. Each one retains the shape and size of the motif, but moves it within the plane.

The simplest isometry is the *translation*, which slides the motif along in one direction. Every pattern uses translations to move the cell across the plane. With our imaginary lamina we slide it across the plane to the nearest pattern in one direction, then change direction and move again to the nearest pattern, as shown in Figure 13. With just two movements, used continually, we could cover an infinite plane.

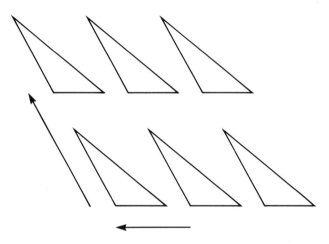

Figure 13

A *rotation* moves the motif around a point. This centre of rotation may be within the motif, on its edge, or elsewhere in the plane. The *order* of the rotation indicates the extent of the rotation. For example, for a rotation of order two there would be two ways in which the shape could fit on to itself. Pupils sometimes find rotational symmetry difficult to understand and this may be partly caused by the language we use. A particular source of confusion is the distinction between the symmetry of the motif itself and the symmetry of the pattern. With a motif like the one shown in Figure 14a we could subject it to half a turn (180°) about its central point and it would fit again into its own outline.

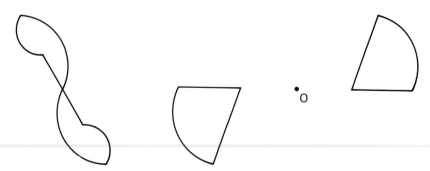

Figure 14a   Motif repeated
with rotation order 2

Figure 14b

With the example in Figure 14b we would have to pivot the whole pattern about the point O which is external to the motif so that the two separate motifs exchange positions. The mathematician tends to treat these two situations as if they were identical, but pupils often perceive them as very different.

A *reflection* flips the motif across an imaginary line. The new motif will be the mirror image of the original, as in Figure 15.

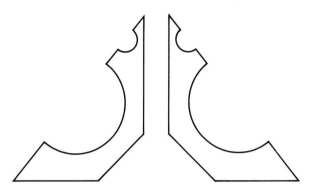

Figure 15

The fourth isometry is a *glide reflection*. It has the effect of combining a translation with a reflection. The image appears to have slid along a line and then 'flipped' across it (see Figure 16).

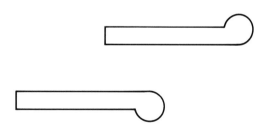

Figure 16

Creating a motif

Starting from any tessellation we can adapt or create a motif by altering each tile in an identical way. Try using hexagonal grid paper and a 10p coin as a starting point. We remove a chunk from one hexagon and assign it to its neighbour (see Figure 17, p. 88).

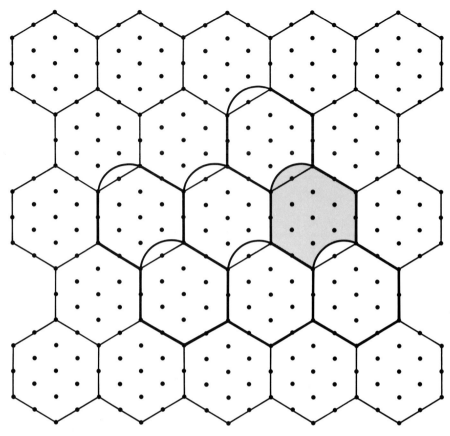

Figure 17

Performing this operation always in the same direction we can create a translation pattern. A similar operation on the sides surrounding a node produces a pattern with rotational symmetry (see Figure 18).

Producing a tessellation which uses glide reflection is a little more difficult but

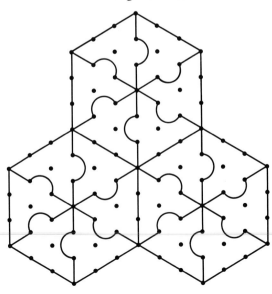

Figure 18

well worth the effort as the results can be very satisfying. Start with an isosceles triangle. Choose one of the equal sides to alter. Then reflect this in the line of symmetry of the triangle (see Figure 19). (The rotations and reflections needed for this work are most easily accomplished with the help of some tracing paper.)

Next, rotate one of the altered lines about its midpoint (see Figure 20).

Alter one half of the third line, reflect it in the line of symmetry of the original triangle, then turn this second half line about its own midpoint (see Figure 21).

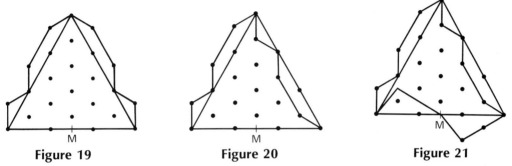

| Figure 19 | Figure 20 | Figure 21 |

The resulting figure should tessellate to produce a pattern consisting of translations and glide reflections. The pattern can be continued by tracing or by cutting out one shape and using it as a template. Figure 22 shows a decorated pattern.

Any motif resulting from a basic grid needs to have 'added on' whatever has been 'cut out', so that the area of the motif is the same as that of the original shape.

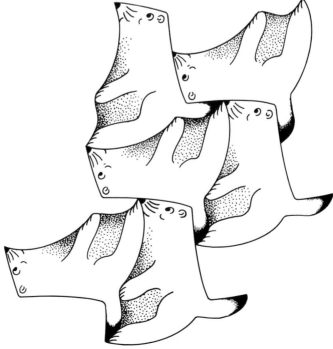

Figure 22

EXERCISES

4 Use hexagonal grid paper and a template to create a tessellation which depends only on translation.

5 Use isometric paper to create a pattern which uses rotation.

6 A reflection followed by a translation can be used to produce a glide reflection. Keeping your ideas simple try your hand at this.

Analysing patterns

A collection of gift wrapping paper, wallpaper patterns or patterned fabric can provide the basis for an investigation of patterns and isometries[1].

In order to analyse the patterns you first need to establish the position of the *cell* (or *period tile*). This involves finding identical points on the tessellation. In this particular case the orientation of the motif is important as well as its position. In each of Figures 28–30 on pp. 94–5 we find the four closest points where the pattern is identical. These are the lattice points and they can be joined to form a period tile. There is a choice of ways in which they can be joined, giving a variety of tessellations. In each case the period tile has an identical area. However, the simplest one to use is that with the shortest possible sides. The period tile is the basic tile from which the whole tessellation can be formed simply by translations. Within this tile there may be more isometries present. (Indeed with Escher's tessellations there are usually plenty more patterns to be found within the period tile.) However, we now have the problem reduced to manageable proportions. If we can establish which transformations have occurred within the tile we can fully analyse the tessellation[2].

EXERCISES

7 Divide a square of side 4 cm into four equal squares of side 2 cm. In one cell create an asymmetrical tile which is simple to copy. Using a template helps to keep lines and curves identical.

Use the tile to create a continuous pattern, as in Figure 23 on p. 91.

Now use the same tile, but create a different pattern.

[1] A useful resource is provided in the series of giftwraps published by H. N. Abrams. In particular: *Giftwraps by Artists: M. C. Escher*

[2] A detailed account of the 17 different pattern types is beyond the scope of this book. Any reader who would like to know more is referred to *Pattern, its Structure and Geometry*, by R. Padwick and T. Walker, which provides a clear and comprehensive account.

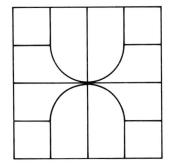 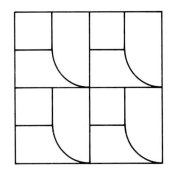

Figure 23

8 Make a collection of repeating patterns on fabric, wrapping paper or wallpaper. For each piece in your collection find the period tile and look for any repeating patterns within the tile. Make notes about your findings. In particular mention any types of symmetry that you notice.

Mathematics in the art room

The artistic side of work on tessellations will be seen by some as a very restricted aspect of art and dismissed as merely 'pattern'. However, for some children this aspect is one of the more appealing forms of art; one with which certain pupils will feel far more confident and there is plenty of scope for creativity in the use of colour and in creating original designs. An obvious link with this work is through the medium of printing.

There are many different ways in which children can be introduced to printing and these can provide an opportunity to explore colour, form and texture. Repeated patterns also utilise mathematical concepts such as parallel lines, angle, rotations, reflections, translations, etc.

Very young children can be introduced to repeated patterns through cutting a set of identical shapes and positioning them along parallel lines to produce a regular pattern (see Figure 24).

Figure 24 Repeating patterns

Printing with potatoes, leaves or junk material such as cotton reels can provide children with the chance to experiment with different orientation of shapes (see Figure 25).

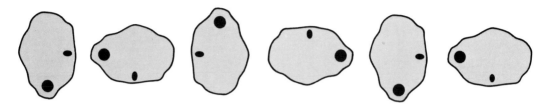

Figure 25   Potato prints

Lino cuts produce a pleasing effect, but the tools used can cause problems in terms of classroom management. A simpler alternative is to use polystyrene tiles. Designs can be made on these using an ordinary biro. If a reflection is needed for a repeat pattern it can be created with the use of tracing paper. Alternatively the design could be created on a piece of paper folded in four with carbon paper in between. When the paper is unfolded the four quadrants will provide the original design and its three variations. These four tiles together produce a motif with two-fold reflective symmetry. This can then be used as a block to cover the page with a printed pattern. Experimentation with the position and orientation of the block will produce a variety of effects.

The method described is very similar to the approach taken in patchwork to design quilts, etc. A set of squares, triangles, hexagons or rhombuses are used to create a block. Within this block there may be symmetry (rotational or reflective) or it may be asymmetrical. When the block is repeated the choice is again available to incorporate symmetry into the design or not.

Printing a motif on to a large piece of paper or card introduces the idea of an infinite plane possibly more effectively than can be done in a 'normal' mathematical classroom situation. When the child reaches the edge of the paper and has a gap left, he or she will need to make a final print which goes partly on and partly off the edge of the paper, reinforcing the idea of an infinite plane.

Consider the task of producing a repeated pattern through printing from a polystyrene tile with an original design. The tile will be used edge to edge to ensure that the pattern repeats in a regular way. The design will be limited to some extent by the choice of shape we make for the tile. If we stay with squares and rectangles, the patterns will repeat in straight lines in two directions, though these could be staggered to produce a more varied effect. If, however, we start off with a regular hexagon for our tile, or a triangle of any sort, then the pattern will look quite different. For a more haphazard effect an irregular quadrilateral could be used. It will produce a repeated pattern, but one of a far more unorthodox type.

EXERCISES

9 Make a set of identical patchwork blocks. If you prefer, card replicas of blocks can be used. Wrapping paper can be used to represent the fabric. Experiment with arrangements for the blocks. Keep a record of your designs. Figure 26 shows some examples.

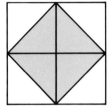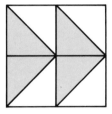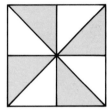

Figure 26 Patchwork patterns

10 On a square piece of lino create an asymmetrical motif. Experiment with different ways to produce repeating patterns using this block, as in Figure 27.

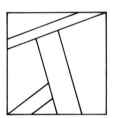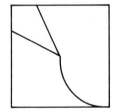

Figure 27 Lino tiles used for printing

11 Cut out some corrugated card shapes. Arrange them on a larger piece of card which is square or hexagonal in shape. (You can use either side to vary the texture.) Use your tile to produce a rubbing. Then move the tile to an adjacent position and continue in this way keeping the pattern regular.

One interesting area of exploration is the technique of overprinting. This allows for exploration of colour combinations and tone. In mathematical terms it also offers a chance to look at areas of overlap between different shapes. In artistic terms we might look at different colour effects and the types of shape which can be produced. In mathematics we might be more interested to know how many different types of shape can be produced from combining, say, a square with a triangle.

Studying Escher's work

There are several books which contain collections of Escher's work. One, which is particularly useful, contains a set of sixteen giftwraps using his designs (see footnote on p. 90). The latter provides a useful collection for analysing the patterns he created. One of the simplest patterns shows a bird whose image is created from a square period tile (see Figure 28).

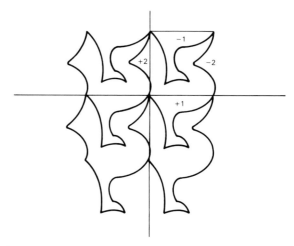

Figure 28   © 1990 M. C. Escher Heirs/Cordon Art – Baarn – Holland

The motif is created by removing a section vertically to create legs, leaving the head and tail shape (1), and horizontally a section is removed to form a nice wide tail (2), leaving the breast and beak clearly defined.

It is quite rare to find such a simple design used by Escher. One of the others contained in this collection shows a butterfly. Shaded ones fly across the page in the usual horizontal orientation, whilst their white compatriots are rotated through 90° (see Figure 29).

The period tile for this pattern is a square containing the equivalent of four butterflies. The edge of the butterfly's wing is rotated through 180° about the midpoint of the side of the square to form the head of the adjacent butterfly. A very similar motif is used in quite a different way in another pattern (see Figure 30).

Here the butterflies have six as their order of rotation, and the design demands three colours to identify one butterfly from another. An analysis of the pattern shows us a grid of parallelograms each made up of two equilateral triangles. Within each triangle we have three butterflies flying around with rotational symmetry, order three. Breaking the triangle into three equal trapezia may help us to understand further how the motif was designed.

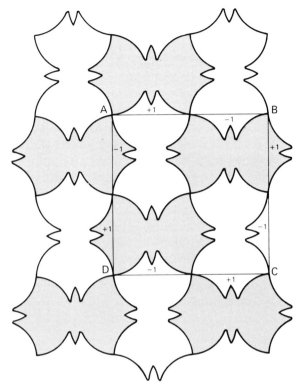

Figure 29   © 1990 M. C. Escher Heirs/Cordon Art – Baarn – Holland

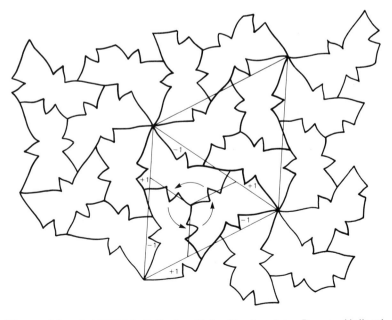

Figure 30   © 1990 M. C. Escher Heirs/Cordon Art – Baarn – Holland

EXERCISE

12 Choose one of Escher's tessellations and find the period tile for the design. Use tracing paper to see how the design 'works'. Use a similar method to design your own tessellating motif.

In writing this chapter I have tried to select exercises which fit 'comfortably' into the mathematics and art programmes which are currently in schools. I am not suggesting a radical and innovative rethink of the curriculum, but I am hoping that the chapter will suggest ways in which a thematic approach could be used in schools, so that teachers with different areas of subject expertise might share their knowledge and plan together to provide a meaningful experience for their pupils. My sub-headings of 'mathematics in the art room' and 'art in the mathematics room' are false divisions. The subject clearly spans such administrative separations.

7 Islamic Design

Marilyn Metz

Introduction

The history of Islamic art and design is a vast subject, covering many centuries and many countries. Throughout this massive and complex study, however, one factor dominates – that of the essential importance of pattern, sequence and order. This runs as a unifying thread throughout the creative arts and crafts in all Islamic countries, and it is this that makes an investigation of art and design in Islam fascinating to a mathematician.

Islamic art, architecture and design are firmly rooted in religious belief. One of the most fundamental principles underlying the strictest interpretation of the arts and crafts of Islam is that it must be non-figurative. The Koran does not appear specifically to prohibit the representation of living beings; this proscription seems to stem from the writings of the Prophet. The argument, in a very simple form, is as follows: God is the Creator of all; representational art is interpreted as a re-creation of life itself, and therefore an attempt to rival the Creator, which is totally unacceptable. This ban on representation extends not only to images of human beings, but also to those of animals, trees, plants – in fact, any living thing. Because of this veto, artists and craftspeople have, over the centuries, concentrated their talents on producing designs which were concerned with pattern and proportion, sequence and order, and have been drawn together by the unifying idea of composition in abstract decorative art. This focus in itself has close connections with religious faith. Order and proportion are seen as universal laws, and the Islamic artist has striven to produce works which best reflect these God-given tenets, whilst adhering to these laws.

Using rules and following 'mathematical recipes' would seem like a denial of artistic creativity to modern western minds. This denial not only reflects the mistaken attitude that creativity can only develop when unbounded by rules, but also falsely implies that mathematics is solely the routine following of rules and cannot in itself give creative pleasure. I find it sad that our culture polarises art and science in this way. For me, there has always been a great deal of pleasure in looking at pattern and design around me, and this pleasure has only been heightened when discovering mathematical connections. Exploring pattern through Islamic ideas is one of many ways of bridging the gap between the two cultures of art and science. What it may also do is provide a safe environment for children to explore, where, when simple mathematical rules are followed, the result is visually delightful, and where, unlike quite a lot of other school mathematics, the answer is not either right or wrong, but satisfying.

My interest in exploring Islamic design started, as Lesley Jones says in her introduction to this book, when we began to look with students at the symmetry in Islamic patterns. Our starting point here was the configuration of numerals known as the Vedic square, which is made by following a simple set of arithmetic rules. Later, having come across several books which concerned themselves with Islamic art, I realised that there was another starting point – that of geometry. This particular beginning seemed to me to be most elegant in its simplicity; by the use of only a straight-edge and a compass, and using some fundamental geometry, beautiful and elaborate patterns could be created. With the addition of colour, each pattern becomes even more fascinating. Each of these starting points can be used with children, to explore space and shape. In the following two sections I hope to provide some initial ideas, and Albarn et al. (1974), El-Said and Parman (1988) and Paccard (1980) should give many more.

Islamic design and the Vedic square

There are several arrays of numerals which are often used in mathematics classes to explore pattern in number. The Pythagorean square (or 100-square) and the multiplication square are two of these, and they provide many interesting ways of looking at pattern in the number system which we use. The Vedic square offers another framework for looking at patterns, and one which is visually interesting and stimulating.

The particular arrangement of numerals known as the Vedic square seems to have become part of Islamic mathematics via Hindu tradition, and was the basis of a whole mathematical system which contained a numerical model of the universe. Integrated into Islamic culture, the visual patterns that are formed by the numbers in the squares appear in many different kinds of ancient and modern design. The fact that the numerals themselves are 'our' numerals only serves to highlight the fact that our number system has a Hindu–Arabic history and is not solely based upon Western European culture.

Generating the square involves only simple multiplication and addition. The numbers 1 to 9 are arranged in rows and columns as shown in Figure 1, p. 99. To fill in the rest of the spaces, multiply the number at the top of the column by the number at the left-hand side of the row. This is straightforward for the first few spaces, as shown in Figure 2. When the product of the two numbers is greater than 9, add the two digits of the product together. For example, column

6 and row 4 produce 24; 2 + 4 = 6, so 6 is entered in that space; column 8 and row 7 produce 56; 5 + 6 = 11; 1 + 1 = 2, so 2 is entered in that space.

Figure 3 shows the completed square.

1	2	3	4	5	6	7	8	9
2								
3								
4								
5								
6								
7								
8								
9								

Figure 1

1	2	3	4	5	6	7	8	9
2	4	6	8					
3	6	9						
4	8			6				
5								
6								
7							2	
8								
9								

Figure 2

1	2	3	4	5	6	7	8	9
2	4	6	8	1	3	5	7	9
3	6	9	3	6	9	3	6	9
4	8	3	7	2	6	1	5	9
5	1	6	2	7	3	8	4	9
6	3	9	6	3	9	6	3	9
7	5	3	1	8	6	4	2	9
8	7	6	5	4	3	2	1	9
9	9	9	9	9	9	9	9	9

Figure 3

Perhaps the first patterns to emerge are those of the numbers in the rows and columns, and initially the numerals seem to have little, if any, spatial pattern, apart from the arrangement of the 9s around the bottom and right-hand borders. But if you look a little more closely, and remember that 9 seems to be significant, you can find shapes that the numerals make within the square.

The shape that the 2s make is shown in Figure 4 on p. 100, and 7s in Figure 5. The 6s and 3s make the shapes shown in Figure 6.

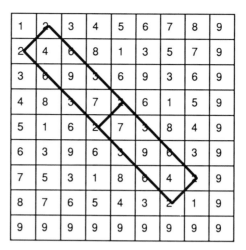

Figure 4

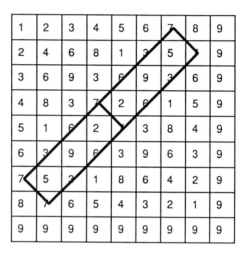

Figure 5

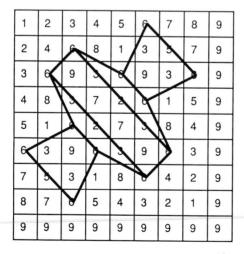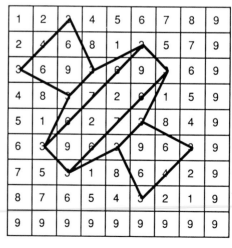

Figure 6

What about the 4s and 5s? And the 1s and 8s?

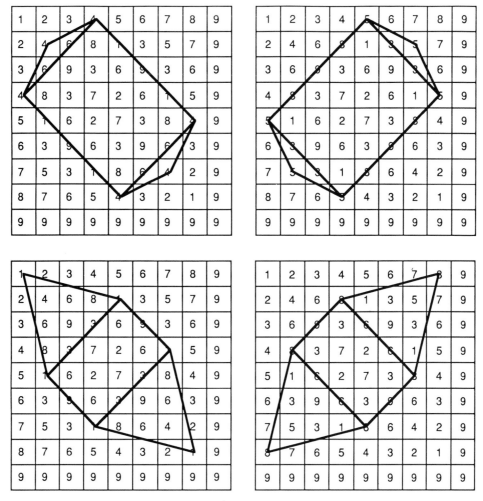

Figure 7

Discovering the symmetry of these pairs of shapes is interesting in itself, but also of interest is that each of the pairs, when totalled, make 9, which is, in a sense, the 'odd number out'. But nine has many traditional and mystical connections – the nine lives of a cat, the nine muses, ninepins, nine-men's morris. And 7, in the centre of the square, is said to have many magical properties.

Having generated these shapes and recognised their connections, further investigations can develop. Tiling designs can be created by repeating the shapes, either on their own or by combining them and tiling the result.

Figure 8 on p. 102 is a tiling of the design obtained by joining the 1s.

Figure 9 is a tiling of the design obtained by combining 2s and 6s.

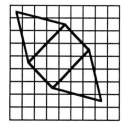

Figure 8

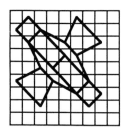

Figure 9

Using colour in different ways opens up more possibilities, which I will leave to you to discover! The shapes created by linking numbers in this way are reminiscent of traditional Islamic patterns which often appear in wall or floor mosaics.

There is a link which connects the exploration of patterns through the arrangement of numbers in the Vedic square, and exploring Islamic design through simple geometry. The link is the circle. The circle has important symbolism not only in Islamic culture, but also in our own Western European culture. It is a mark of a whole, a completeness, and also a symbol of the world, the universe, and of infinity. As such, it has an important place in the work of Islamic artists and craftspeople.

Using the nine numerals of the Vedic square and arranging them equally spaced around a circle, it is possible to produce other basic shapes if you join the numbers according to their order in the rows of the Vedic square. For instance, using the circle join the numbers on it in the order in which they appear in the fifth row of the square (5 1 6 2 7 3 8 4 9) as in Figure 10.

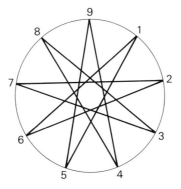

Figure 10

Try it with other rows and experiment with tiling these shapes to produce overall designs. An example of this is shown in Figure 11, using the design made by joining the numbers in the second row of the square (2 4 6 8 1 3 5 7 9).

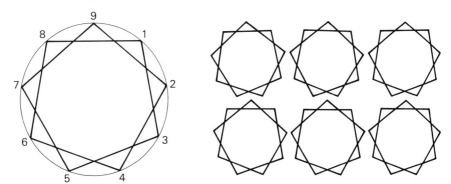

Figure 11

Any of the activities described above would make splendid investigations into pattern, taking the Vedic square as the starting point, and also make a strong link between looking at pattern in number and the creation of Islamic designs. Much of the work could be extended through use of colour, and expanded into the areas of fabric design, patchwork and tapestry stitching.

Islamic design and shape

An alternative route into Islamic pattern-making is equally rich in potential, and throws a fascinating light on the early use of very simple geometry in design and architecture.

Before the introduction of zero in the Indian number system, in the eighth century AD, and the adoption of this system by Islamic cultures, there was no commonly recognised way of calculating, and therefore no standard way of using number to measure space or shape. This absence of a standard approach, however, certainly does not seem to have inhibited the creation of much fine and elaborate architecture. Much more simple approaches were used, often based upon some arbitrary unit of measure such as the hand, foot or stride. An object itself, such as a length of string, could also be the unit, and could then be halved, quartered, etc., in order to produce necessary related measures. These methods are still in everyday use in some societies, and I think you will find that we also employ similar measuring techniques in everyday life. Measuring, however, to us, is formally associated with numbers, and school geometry seems inevitably connected with standard measurement, often of lines and angles. When opening a school mathematics book at random, I came across several examples which show this to be true. 'In the sunshine, a stick which is 1 m high has a shadow of length 0.8 m on the horizontal ground. At the same time a flagpole has a shadow which is 4.8 m long. How high is the flagpole?' 'The area of a triangle is 90 cm^2 and the base is 12 cm. What is the perpendicular height?'

If we take a step back from this conventional approach to shape, and look instead at ancient methods of measuring space, we immediately find a wealth of absorbing mathematics as well as another route into creating pattern which has been, for many centuries, and still is, one of the primary methods by which traditionally based Islamic craftspeople produce their masterpieces.

As mentioned before, the circle is an important symbol, and this is where we start. There is evidence that in ancient Egypt, architects and engineers used rope-and-peg techniques to mark out and measure the plans of buildings. These methods were absorbed by early Islamic craftspeople, and, with the emphasis that Islamic design puts on shape and pattern, became the traditional way to generate designs without any mathematical calculations. The methods of generating many regular polygons, using only a compass and a straight-edge, basing them on a circle, are described below. We can start with a square.

Draw a line and, with the centre at any point on this line, draw a circle. Call the centre M, and the two points where the line cuts the circle A and B.
Use the compass to bisect the line AB and mark the points C and D on the circumference.
With the same radius as that of the circle (MA), draw segments slightly larger than semicircles using A, B, C, and D as centres.
Join the points where the segments intersect with straight lines to make the square (see Figure 12a, p. 104).

It is also possible to create a square inside the circle, by joining the points where the diagonals of the large square cut the circle (see Figure 12b), or by joining points ABCD.
This square is obviously a very simple tile, and could be used to tessellate a space as it is. But, with the addition of just a few more lines, we can create much more interesting designs. For instance, see Figure 13.

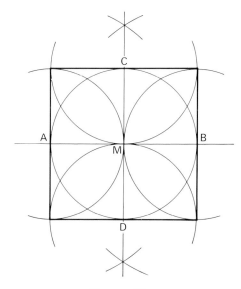

Figure 12a

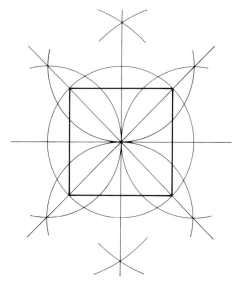

Figure 12b

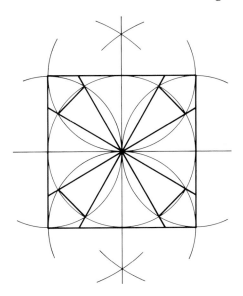

Figure 13

Try creating a repeat pattern using this motif as in Figure 14.

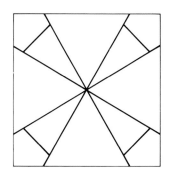

Figure 14

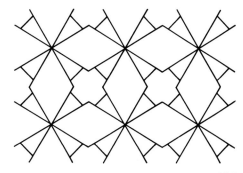

Figure 15 shows a different motif and pattern.

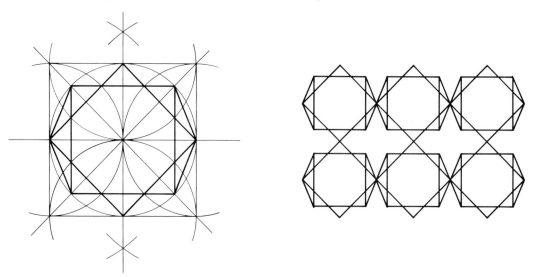

Figure 15

From the simple beginning of the square, we can begin to see how elaborate patterns can be generated. Similar starting points can be the pentagon and hexagon, and these, too can be produced from a circle. First, the regular pentagon:

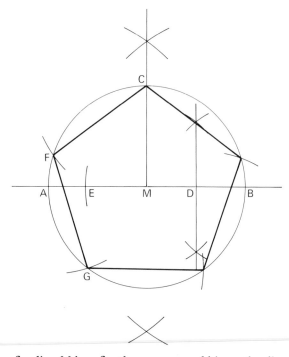

Figure 16

Draw a circle of radius MA as for the square, and bisect the diameter AB, but this time mark only C where the bisecting line cuts the circle.
Bisect radius MB at D.

With centre at D, and a radius of CD, draw an arc cutting MA at E.
With centre at C, and a radius of CE, draw an arc cutting the circumference of the circle at F.
Join CF, which is one side of the pentagon.
To make the other sides of the shape, use a radius of CF, and centre at F, and cut the circumference at G. Continue in this way until you have marked all of the points, joining them to create the pentagon, as in Figure 16.

The regular hexagon is a much more straightforward construction.
Draw a circle with any radius. The radius of this circle will divide its circumference into six equal sections, thus giving you the points with which to draw the hexagon, as shown in Figure 17.

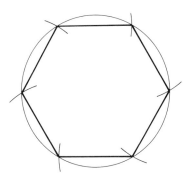

Figure 17

Many other regular shapes can easily be generated from these three (see Figure 18). Drawing the diagonals of the square will give you the other four points on the circumference of a circle so that you can produce a regular octagon. Bisecting the sides of a hexagon will give you a dodecagon, and similarly a decagon can be created from a pentagon, and so on.

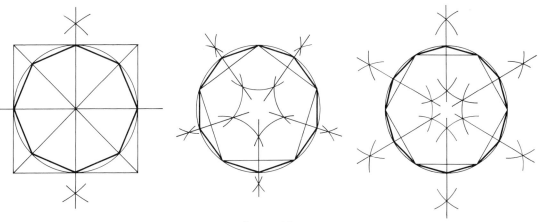

Figure 18

Using these shapes inscribed in a square, many exciting designs can be made in the way in which the patterns in Figures 14 and 15 were created. But you do not need to restrict your basic tile to that of the square. All tilings can be analysed by establishing the basic tile, which will be a parallelogram of some kind. Try using different parallelograms as the tiling unit. For example, consider Figure 19.

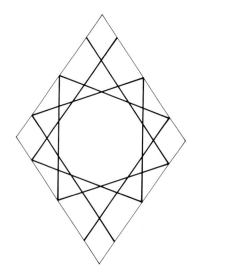 

Figure 19

And, of course, the regular hexagon, Figure 20, will tile as well.

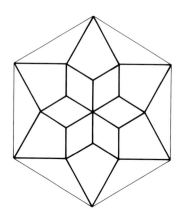 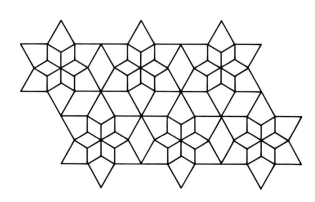

Figure 20

Again, the use of colour can expand these investigations in an almost unlimited way.

Until the very day of writing this I had tried, but failed, to make a link between the circular arrangement of the Vedic square numerals and the generation of Islamic designs using compass and straight-edge. Escaping from my word-processor for a while, I happened to meet an artist friend, who has long been interested in mathematical ideas, and once taught in primary schools. I am indebted to him for sharing with me his method of generating a regular nonagon, which is the connection I needed. His method is unconventional, because it depends upon making a three-dimensional shape as an intermediate stage, but is well-tried, having been used in many primary classrooms. The method is described as follows.

First, make a regular decagon, as shown in Figure 21, by generating a pentagon and bisecting the sides. Then, after marking the radii, cut out the decagon. Cut along one radius to the centre and fold along all the others. You can now tuck one triangle of the decagon underneath another and stick it down. Next, lay the figure on paper and draw around the remaining nine sides – you have a regular nonagon. To find the centre of the circle within which this nonagon will sit, bisect two of the shape's sides. The point of intersection of the bisections is the centre of that circle.

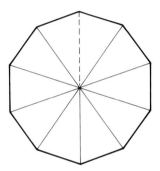

Figure 21

There may be more mathematically conventional ways of producing the nonagon – perhaps some readers might like to take up the challenge and try for themselves! There seems to be evidence that it is possible; although El-Said and Parman have not included an analysis of 7, 9 or 11 sided regular polygons in their excellent book, they do state that the principles of their construction are the same as those which they describe for other regular polygons. I am sure that Islamic craftspeople did not use this method for their construction, but personally, I find my friend's method elegant in its simplicity, and also fun!

As well as using the Vedic square, or a compass and straight-edge to produce Islamic designs, it is also possible to analyse examples of Islamic patterns, and thus gain some insight into how the creators of the designs might have conceived and constructed their work. Plate 7.1 shows a photograph of a tiled floor in the Red Fort in Lahore, taken on a recent visit to Pakistan. The Red Fort was built by the Moghul ruler Akbar in the late sixteenth century, though this floor probably dates from a seventeenth century re-building by Shah Jahan, who also built the Taj Mahal.

The tile which is the unit of this beautiful tessellation can be fairly easily drawn (see Figure 22, p. 110). First, find four points on the floor which are identical – in this case I have chosen the centres of the small white four-pointed stars. If you join these points together, you can see that the basic tile is a square

109

(allowing for the perspective in the photograph). Generating a square with compass and straight-edge, and adding several more construction lines produces a figure from which you can derive the combination of shapes which, when laid together, will produce the same design as that of the photograph. When I tried this method, I was surprised and delighted that the tile can be made by drawing only eight lines (with breaks in them). Which are the eight?

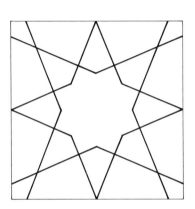

Figure 22

Practical considerations

There are some practical classroom factors which need to be considered when embarking upon any of the activities outlined above, and, if borne in mind, will mean that the children will gain much satisfaction from their investigations.

Good tools are the first pre-requisite. A reliable compass, sound straight-edge and well-sharpened pencils are essential, as is an effective eraser. There is nothing more frustrating than trying to work more carefully than your equipment will allow. I must emphasise that an uncalibrated straight-edge should be used, so that there is no temptation to slip into using standard linear measurements when making the designs. A plentiful supply of good-quality tracing paper is useful, too, for trying out the ideas described in both of the previous sections. Tracing paper can be used as an overlay on a main copy of the Vedic square, so that the numerals do not appear on the designs created, and can also be used to make copies of the circle-based patterns, although access to a photocopier which will make reductions is more desirable. Sharp scissors will be needed to cut out the individual tiles, and a good quality adhesive is important when assembling the final tessellations. Paints, coloured pencils or felt-tip pens could be used to colour the patterns, depending upon their size.

Although the emphasis here has been on generating designs by hand, there are one or two computer programs available which create tiles and repeating patterns. Amongst these are Islam (Junior Maths, Earosoft)[1] and Mosaic (HILDICH)[2].

Using one of these programs would give children the opportunity to produce their own designs quickly and accurately, and also to explore colour. Using LOGO is also a possibility, but would certainly involve angle and line measurement, and thus would change the emphasis of the work considerably.

This chapter has only shown a very small number of the possible Islamic and Islamic-inspired designs that can be created. Using simple mathematical starting points, it is possible to create many diverse patterns – in fact I have had a great deal of difficulty choosing examples to include here. Much of my inspiration has been gained from a handful of beautiful and absorbing books, including, Albarn et al (1974), El-Said and Parman (1988) and Paccard (1980). The book by Andre Paccard is inspiring, both in its colour plates, and in the description of how craftspeople in Morocco create their magnificent mosaics. *The Language of Pattern* is one of the books which first inspired Lesley Jones and myself, as is *Geometric Concepts in Islamic Art*, from which many of the ideas in this chapter grew. I recommend them, and hope that they give you as much pleasure and as much inspiration as they continue to give me.

Figures 1 to 9 were generated on an Apple Macintosh Plus computer, using the program MacDraw.

EXERCISES

1 Using only a pair of compasses, a pencil and an uncalibrated ruler, make a regular octagon. What different designs can you make by joining points according to different sets of rules?

2 Use one of the number patterns from the Vedic square to produce a lino cut 'tile'. Design a repeating pattern using your tile.

3 Make a regular nonagon using the technique described on p. 108.

4 Work with the computer program Islam (Junior Maths, Earosoft) to produce a repeating pattern. Using this design, choose your own medium to create the same pattern.

[1] From Earosoft, The Resource Centre, Back Hill, Ely, Cambs. CB7 4DA

[2] From: Advisory Unit for Microtechnology in Education, Endymion Road, Hatfield, Herts. AL10 8AU

5 Using reference books, find some Islamic patterns. Choose one particular pattern, study it carefully and use compasses and uncalibrated ruler to copy the basic tile.

6 Use LOGO to create a geometric design; then produce a procedure which will repeat this design, covering the screen.

Complex Art

8

John Bradshaw

Fractals

The Mandelbrot Set broods in silent complexity at the centre of a vast two-dimensional sheet of numbers called the complex plane. When a certain operation is applied repeatedly to the numbers, the ones outside the set flee to infinity. The numbers inside remain to drift or dance about. Close to the boundary, minutely choreographed wanderings mark the onset of the instability. Here is an infinite regress of detail that astonishes us with its variety, its complexity and its strange beauty.

Dewdney, 1985

Figure 1   The Mandelbrot Set

It is unusual, to say the least, to encounter a topic which currently engages the attention of professional mathematicians and yet is accessible to school pupils. Nevertheless, the seeds of one such branch of mathematics had been sown over sixty years ago by the French mathematicians Gaston Julia and Pierre Fatou. Part of the problem for them had been the vast number of calculations needed before any satisfactory visual representation of the mathematics could be realised. Much more recently in the USA, Benoit Mandelbrot, a former student of Julia, furthered their work with the aid of computers and by 1980 had also discovered what is now known as the Mandelbrot Set.

Most people knew little or nothing of all this until the work of H. O. Pietgen and P. H. Richter from the Centre for Complex Dynamics at the University of Bremen was shown in this country in a travelling exhibition organised by the Goethe–Institut in 1985. Thanks to a series of articles by Keith Devlin in *The Guardian* in June and July of that year (Devlin, 1985, p. 15), the distinctive chaotic images – if not the theory behind complex dynamics – gained a far wider audience. The exhibition, appropriately entitled 'Schoenheit im Chaos' in Germany but oddly billed here as 'Frontiers of Chaos', made a big impression on many people. Stunning metre square images in a full spectrum of intense colour were produced in collaboration with the IBM laboratories at Boblingen in West Germany and were so 'out of this world' that most of us regarded it as purely the province of those with access to mainframe computers with fancy colour graphics capabilities!

However, it was not long before the popular science and computer press published programs which would produce similar images on small micro-computers, albeit with significant limitations, but nevertheless actually making it achievable both at school and at home.

One of the many interesting properties of the image of the Mandelbrot Set is that the edge or boundary will always reveal more detail no matter how much it is enlarged. In general, shapes with this property are called *fractals*, although there is a formal mathematical definition. While this sounds an amazing property at first encounter, in fact, fractal edges are far more common in nature than the apparently familiar straight and simple curved edges that we see and draw. A commonly quoted example is the coastline of Britain. At a pinch, many people can draw a recognisable freehand sketch of the country to convey useful information to others. A small scale map would give you enough information to be able to estimate the perimeter of the mainland to within, say, ten per cent of the 'correct' value. A larger scale map would improve the accuracy, but would involve you in having to include estuaries and small bays. Ordnance Survey maps will give much more detail with an accurate scale of 1 : 50 000 but the necessary inclusion of every promontory and creek will increase the initial estimate considerably. Reference to 1 : 25 000 scale OS will not only reveal more detail but push the perimeter estimate higher still. Effectively, the coastline of Britain is a fractal because the closer you look, the more detail can be seen. Practically, the process must end when you have negotiated every grain of sand! However, it is possible to conceive of shapes where the enlarging process can be continued forever. In fact they are not so rare, and some simple ones are very easy to draw. But, unlike Slartibartfast's design for Norway – 'Won an award you know. Lovely crinkly edges.' – as chronicled in *The Hitch-Hiker's Guide to the Galaxy*, true fractals do not result from artistic inspiration alone. There has to be a rule or set of rules that are implemented repeatedly, each time modifying that done by the previous iteration. If the process is continued indefinitely then the result will be a fractal.

These fractal-generating rules can be very simple indeed, in which case, the result is sometimes predictable. However, it only takes a minor complication or a slight twist in the rules for the results to be quite amazing.

A common illustration of one of the simplest and most predictable fractals is the so-called snowflake curve shown in Figure 2.

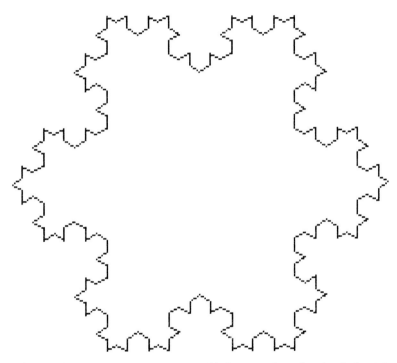

Figure 2   Convex snowflake: the third generation of a simple fractal

Because the fractal shown is being built up, rather than already in existence and is being more and more closely examined, any drawing made of it must, by definition, be only an early stage in its formation. The true fractal is of the nth generation where n is infinite. In fact the one drawn above is only the third generation. Starting with an equilateral triangle, the rule is that each side is equally divided into three and the centre third is replaced by two sides of a small equilateral triangle (see Figure 3, p. 116).

At each subsequent stage, every centre line segment is replaced according to the rule and the process is continued indefinitely. After the original triangle, the first two generations are shown in Figure 4, p. 116.

Figure 3

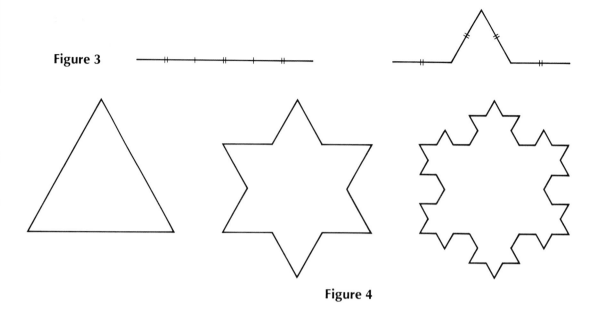

Figure 4

This is a useful classroom activity in that it encompasses quite a number of skills and concepts. Accurate pencil, ruler and compass work are required and as the process continues the pupil is forcibly made aware of the effects of cumulative error. Pattern spotting, in that the design is based on smaller and smaller isometric grids so that all edges should belong to one of three sets of parallel lines means that the effects of errors can be continually monitored and appropriate corrections made. If A3 paper is issued, an original triangle of side 27 cm is most suitable and gives at least four generations without having to start estimating thirds. Some pupils will draw the original triangle which nearly fills the page and jump to the conclusion that it will surely fall off the edge before long. Having been encouraged to continue nevertheless, many will obtain an early illustration of a process tending to a limit in a very practical manner, as well as a glimpse of infinite sequences. Pupils seem to find both the process and the results appealing – the first time. While variations of the rule may well suggest themselves, the labour of actually doing it is daunting and so, as Mandelbrot himself found, a computer is really called for.

Although it is of course possible to program this in BASIC, it is quite a lengthy listing and a far more elegant approach is to use LOGO. Here is a suggestion written in Logotron LOGO consisting of the procedure SNOW which calls the recursive procedure FLAKE three times (in order to account for the three sides of the original equilateral triangle).

```
TO SNOW :LENGTH :LIMIT

CS PU BK 350 PD
REPEAT 3 [FLAKE :LENGTH :LIMIT RIGHT 120]
END
```

```
TO  FLAKE  :LENGTH  :LIMIT

IF  :LENGTH<:LIMIT  [FORWARD  :LENGTH  STOP]
FLAKE  :LENGTH/3  :LIMIT
LEFT  60
FLAKE  :LENGTH/3  :LIMIT
RIGHT  120
FLAKE  :LENGTH/3  :LIMIT
LEFT  60
FLAKE  :LENGTH/3  :LIMIT
END
```

This will draw the convex snowflake curve, and suggested starting parameters are 729 and 81 although most of the fun is to be gained by individual investigation. Interchanging RIGHT and LEFT in FLAKE will produce the concave snowflake shown in Figure 5, and introducing different commands often results in more interesting fractal shapes, especially if a random command is also built in.

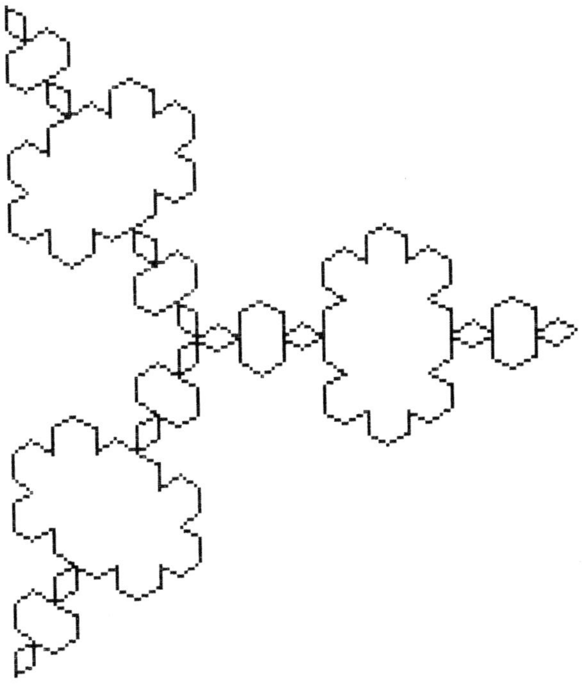

Figure 5   Concave snowflake

Other simple fractals are to be found on Leapfrogs posters[1], but for a more do-it-yourself approach, Noss (1985, pp. 30–5) gives a LOGO procedure for another fractal called the Koch curve, as in Figure 6, and goes on to discuss random fractals.

[1] Fractal posters are available from: Leapfrogs, Tarquin Publications, Stradbroke, Diss, Norfolk IP21 5JP

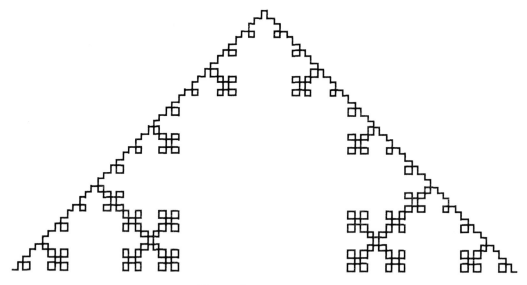

Figure 6   Koch curve

Backhouse (1986, pp. 34–8) also describes the Koch curve together with further fractals including the Menger sponge and lists a versatile BBC BASIC program to produce them, leaving plenty of scope for 'what if…' investigations.

Chaos

Science and aesthetics are in agreement about what is actually missing in technical objects as compared to natural objects: it is the luxury of an appropriate portion of irregularity, disorder and unpredictability. This insight could help us in a very basic way to give technology, on which we are more and more dependent for survival, a humane face.

Eilenberger, 1985

In the examples of simple fractals given earlier, there are no surprises: if you've seen a bit, then you've seen it all! They all exhibit at least one axis of bilateral symmetry as well as their intrinsic regularity and so at a fairly superficial level usually have an immediate attraction for many children. However, this very predictability as a result of self-replication is its downfall – it's pretty boring after a while, although a similar simple fractal design did provide the design for the author's Christmas cards one year.

If, however, the fractal-generating rules are such that more than one option is available at each iteration, for example there may be a series of conditions controlling the next move, then the overall form that the shape takes may well be quite unpredictable. Although the shape will still have fractal edges, the exact self-replication element is missing, at least at first glance. So, coupled with the property of possessing infinite detail, there is a chaotic element in place of the rigid predictability and this results in the endless variety to be found when investigating such strange objects as the Mandelbrot Set (see Figure 7).

Figure 7

It is this endless variety, or amazing complexity, which provides most of the appeal here. It is so unlike the familiar geometrical objects that we normally deal with. It is truly at the other end of the spectrum from, say, a straight line. A straight line will appear identical no matter how much any segment is enlarged: we say it has total self-similarity and you can't get much more 'un-complex' than that. Slightly more interesting shapes such as a circle have only limited complexity and the more closely you examine them the less complex

119

they appear – smaller and smaller portions of a circle successively look more and more like straight line segments. A chaotic fractal, on the other hand, is so complex that tiny parts of it appear as complex as the whole. Common sense would seem to indicate that, for all shapes, complexity diminishes as magnification increases, and yet if you start from 'infinite complexity', as with the Mandelbrot Set, then naturally enough, repeated magnifications will reveal no lessening of complexity. It is this very complexity that reflects the local unpredictability of chaos. Only *local*, because although no details ever stay constant, there is always an *overall* structure or shape to be discerned. This is in much the same way as physical laws hold despite the inherent uncertainty over the position and velocity of a body's constituent subatomic particles at any given moment. Similarly, it is accepted that while individual people may well behave in quite random or at least unpredictable ways, nevertheless it is perfectly valid to make overall predictions on a statistical basis about the population as a whole if a long enough time span is taken. Weather forecasting is yet another example of a system where local behaviour is apparently chaotic and, unfortunately for us, rather unpredictable. However, with galling hindsight, overall patterns can be seen.

So it is with the Mandelbrot Set. Diving into the infinite detail of the fractal edges of the set, the macro 'bread-man' image (see Plate 8.1) is soon lost to view as a host of fresh images clamour for our attention. Continuing the 'magnification' we see evermore fascinating variations on (soon to be almost familiar) themes until a tiny gap appears and slowly develops into what is obviously a tiny copy of the whole set! (See Plate 8.2.)

It is not an exact copy, however. Chaos rules at this deep level and yet there is still an underlying order and the property of self-similarity remains intact. In fact there is, and you probably guessed it by now, an infinite number of these micro bread-men to be found and investigated.

Abstract mathematical art

Luck differs greatly from Art, and yet creates many things that are like it.
Ion of Chios

So, as a consequence of this relatively new branch of mathematics, with the aid of a computer and an appropriate program, almost anybody can produce a vast number of bright, colourful and very complicated pictures. Most people who see them find them pleasing to the eye to the extent that images from the Mandelbrot Set are now to be found on record covers, tee-shirts and on the covers of College prospectuses and magazines[1]. However, the question has to be asked: 'Is it art?'

[1] For example, see the cover of the September 1988 issue of *Mathematics in School*, a journal of the Mathematical Association.

Artists walk around with their eyes open. Everything they see can be taken as grist to the mill and the images are subconsciously sorted and either stored or discarded. Any fresh source of images may well be welcomed either as an inspiration for work to follow or even as a piece in its own right. It is not uncommon, for example, to see a carefully arranged collection of 'found' objects presented as a piece of art. Assuming it does in fact have some merit in that it is pleasing, evocative or thought-provoking, it is consequently considered no less worthy than a realistic representation of a person or a landscape executed in oils. The essence of the matter would seem to be that it is the *selection* of the image in the first place that constitutes much of the essential work of the artist. The selection having taken place, the image may or may not be modified, processed, re-interpreted or whatever and much of that stage may well be technical rather than artistic.

The most obvious example of this is seen in photography. Having the knowledge of how to handle a camera correctly, understanding depth of field, 'f' stops and filters is a necessary but not a sufficient condition for the creation of a portfolio worth looking at. It is the selection of the image – the subject itself together with the orientation, perspective, frame, and decisions about what to include and what not to include – that makes a picture rather than a snapshot. The technical element is an essential prerequisite and is teachable. The art is in the selection of both the image and its subsequent treatment. If then we regard the pictures that have been generated on the monitor screen by the computer as being analogous to the view seen through a camera's viewfinder, it is presumably equally valid to go through the selection and subsequent processes with the reasonable expectation that the end result will be accepted as being art. Now, therefore, the artist has a new-found source of stimulus and can choose from a wealth of artificial shapes and images as well as natural ones, and can subsequently work with selected facets as in the past.

Whether or not the Mandelbrot Set is, in fact, a natural phenomenon is a moot point. Certainly, we seem to have here the results of a process which is described entirely by mathematics, then realised by machine, and which often turn out to be intrinsically beautiful. The rings of Saturn could not be appreciated or even seen until the development of suitable hardware and the skills to use it. In the same way, these chaotic fractals have only recently come to our attention. So can they justifiably be termed 'natural'? Perhaps they are a mathematical equivalent of a glorious sunset.

This infinity of different images is totally computer-generated and not human- or machine-inspired. As already discussed, the only scope for exercising aesthetic judgement is in the selection of the image itself and then the allocation of colour and any subsequent processes. This is fundamentally different from most computer art which usually either employs random elements or merely uses the machine as a sophisticated paintbrush. In fact, not one of these images could even be drawn during one person's lifetime without the help of a computer. What is more, even with the help of the most powerful computer existing, no image can ever actually be finished, as the detail continues unabated, decreasing in size forever.

The colour plates are photographs of the monitor screen and provide very vivid results, but a good colour dot-matrix printer can produce pleasing effects as well. Black and white printing is probably the most accessible however, and some screen-dump routines offer options as to the size, density and toning of the printing and so, reversed or negative and even half-tone effects can be tried.

Figure 8   Half-tone screen dump of a low resolution image

Often the removal of the half-tones brings out strong patterns that were partially hidden by all the mass of detail on the original screen. While it will be possible to modify the program itself to produce the effect on the screen, it is much easier to risk another sheet of printer paper and experiment with the screen-dump parameters. Such very strong monochrome images lend themselves much more to subsequent processing than do the more complete originals, as the intricate details can become blurred and so detract from the overall effect. Such techniques could include photo-screen printing or the building up of large-scale repeat patterns with the aid of a photocopier, or even a pastiche of such images.

If the expertise is available to modify or rewrite the programs then naturally the scope becomes even wider. Just one possibility is to add the representation of a third dimension and immediately the images become a little less abstract and somewhat representational of natural landscapes (see Figure 9) – and so we return to coastlines as being examples of fractal edges.

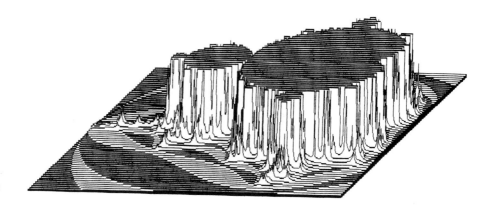

Figure 9

Plotting in the complex plane

Although it is by no means necessary to understand the theoretical basis for the creation of these chaotic fractals – indeed much work still needs to be done before even professional mathematicians have a reasonably complete understanding of the whole field – as stated at the start of this chapter, the basic explanation is within the scope of A-level pupils.

An understanding of the basic theory of complex numbers and the Argand diagram, together with the notion of iterative processes, could reasonably be expected by the second year in the sixth form. Given these, the basic idea to be explained here is of sequentially taking points in the complex plane, applying an iterative test to each one and consequently plotting a point or pixel of a colour arbitrarily allocated to the result of the test. Each point in the plane, usually referred to as 'c', is of course a complex number and is fed into the transformation:

$$z^2 + c \longrightarrow z$$

where z is another complex number but primed with the start value of zero. As the process is repeated over and over again for the particular c in question, z becomes larger (or further from zero) and behaves in one of two possible ways.

It either reaches the value 2 and so inevitably hurtles off to infinity or it settles down and tends to a finite limit. In the latter case, our current c has 'passed the test' and qualifies for membership of the Mandelbrot Set, that is, it can be plotted black in Figure 10.

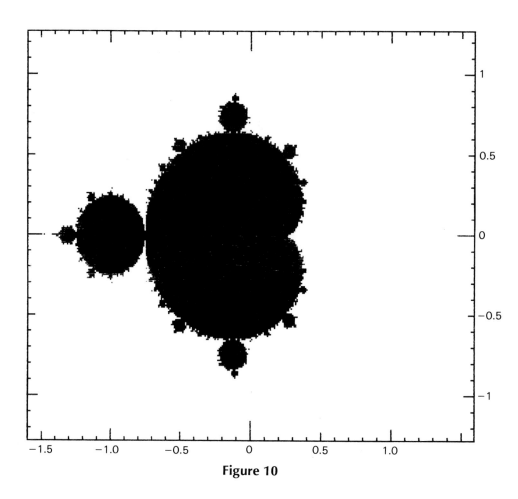

Figure 10

This particular screen-dump was produced on a BBC Model B by Bill Richardson (currently Head of Mathematics at Elgin Academy) as a result of a simple BASIC program he had written. However, much of the fun to be had is in 'zooming in' to the interstices of the fractal edge, so it is much easier, and far less frustrating, to actually use one of the rather more complicated but far more friendly programs that have been published in the specialist computer press. Nevertheless, pupils have written their own for the fun of it and Jason Brown (now studying Computer Science at Aston University) wrote the program in C shown in Figure 11 on p. 125 during his final year at school.

```
/*******************************
 * Basic Mandelbrot Set Plotter *
 *        Written in C          *
 *                              *
 *        By Jason Brown        *
 *          5 May 1988          *
 *******************************/

#define X_SIDE            199       /* Number of pixels along horizontal   */
                                    /* axis of the screen. Really 200      */
                                    /* (0 to 199). Change this to the      */
                                    /* relevant figure for your computer.  */
#define Y_SIDE            199       /* Ditto for vertical axis.            */

main()
{
        double  origin_real = 0.0,    /* Real origin of plot.            */
                origin_imag = 0.0,    /* Imaginary origin of plot.       */
                range = 0.0,          /* Length of a side.               */
                x_gap = 0.0,          /* Gap between points along        */
                                      /* the real axis.                  */
                y_gap = 0.0,          /* Gap between points along        */
                                      /* the imaginary axis.             */
                z_real = 0.0,         /* Real part of z                  */
                z_imag = 0.0,         /* Imaginary part of z             */
                c_real = 0.0,         /* Real part of c                  */
                c_imag = 0.0,         /* Imaginary part of c             */
                size = 0.0,           /* Size of z                       */
                temp = 0.0;           /* Temporary variable used in      */
                                      /* Mandelbrot calulation           */
        int     x = 0,                /* Position along x-axis of screen. */
                y = 0,                /* Position along y-axis of screen. */

                count = 0,            /* Number of iterations that have  */
                                      /* been performed on the current   */
                                      /* pixel.                          */
                max_count;            /* Maximum number of iterations to */
                                      /* perform per pixel.              */

        printf("Real Origin:  ");      /* Get the real part of the origin. */
        scanf("%lf",&origin_real);
        printf("Imaginary Origin:  ");  /* Get the imaginary part of the   */
        scanf("%lf",&origin_imag);      /* origin.                         */
        printf("Side Length:  ");       /* Get the length of a side.       */
        scanf("%lf",&range);
        printf("Maximum Number of Iterations:  ");    /* Get the maximum */
        scanf("%ld",&max_count);                      /* number of       */
                                                      /* iterations per  */
                                                      /* pixel.          */

        graphics();     /* Change the screen to graphics mode.    */
                        /* Replace this with the relevant command */
                        /* for your system.                       */
        printf("\07");  /* Beep to signify the start of the plot. */

        y_gap = range / Y_SIDE;       /* Calculate the gap between pixels */
                                      /* along the imaginary axis.        */
        x_gap = range / X_SIDE;       /* Calculate the gap between pixels */
                                      /* along the real axis.             */

        /* Scan every point on the screen, top-to-bottom, and left-to-right */

        for (y = 0; y <= Y_SIDE; y++)   /* Scan top-to-bottom */
                for (x = 0; x <= X_SIDE; x++)        /* Scan left-to-right */
                {
                        /* In the next line, change the `-' to a `+' if
                           (0,0) is at the bottom left on your computer */
                        c_imag = origin_imag + (y * y_gap);  /* Where are */
                        c_real = origin_real + (x * x_gap);  /* we on the */
                                                             /* Argand    */
                                                             /* diagram?  */
                        z_real = z_imag = 0.0;  /* Don't know z yet. */
                        count = 0;
                        do
                        {
                                /* Calculate the new value of z */
                                temp = 2.0 * z_real * z_imag;
                                z_real = (z_real * z_real) -
                                         (z_imag * z_imag) + c_real;
                                z_imag = temp + c_imag;
                                /* How big is z? */
                                size = (z_real * z_real) + (z_imag * z_imag);
                                count++;
                        }
                        /* If this point is not yet fleeing to infinity, */
                        /* then carry on (as long as iteration limit has */
                        /* not been reached), otherwise, exit the loop.  */
                        while (size < 4.0 && count < max_count);

                        if (count >= max_count)
                                plot(x,y,1);    /* Plot the point on the   */
                                                /* screen. Change this to  */
                                                /* plot the point in       */
                                                /* whatever style you wish. */
                                                /* This will plot bands of */
                                                /* alternating light and   */
                                                /* dark.                   */
                }
        printf("\07");            /* Wakey Wakey, I've finished!            */
        (void) getch();           /* Display picture until a key is pressed */
        text();                   /* Change back to text mode and exit. Alter */
                                  /* this to the relevant command for your  */
                                  /* system.                                */
} /* main */
```

Figure 11

125

As intimated in one of Jason's final 'Rem' statements, on the usual microcomputer it can take a very long time to plot an entire screen – one of the author's early attempts successfully produced an image of the entire set but took over six hours to do so! Although tedious, it is not surprising, as the million pixels on the screen could each require a thousand calculations before a plot is made.

While Dewdney (1985 and 1987) gives very much more detailed explanations of the programming aspects in general, an easy-to-use and ready-made program for the BBC Model B and Master series machines was published in *Acorn User* magazine (Johnson-Davies, 1986, pp. 80–3 and 114–15) which incorporates a novel method to enable the user to see early on if the chosen start coordinates are likely to produce fruitful results. Simultaneously, *BEEBUG* magazine published a similar listing (Crennell, 1986, pp. 6–12) which offered a choice of modes giving either relatively high resolution but few colours and a long plot time or poorer resolution but more colours and 'only 25 minutes' to wait.

All of these programs are, however, severely limited by the speed of the hardware. In a totally different class is the Acorn Archimedes series of machines with the RISC processors. With the increasing number of BBC A3000 micros to be found in schools, use can be made of programs such as the more recent one also listed in *Acorn User* (Fedonczuk, 1988, pp. 103–7 and 122–4). This rather more lengthy program – available on disk – produced the colour images shown in this article: far higher resolution with 128 colours or shades and in only 28 seconds!

A significant recent development in educational software has provided a new microworld in which to investigate the idea of chaos and its associated images. NUMERATOR, a 'mathematical construction kit' produced by Logotron, is a versatile tool which lends itself to assembling feedback systems in a very visual manner. Consequently a pack[1] has been produced in conjunction with the popular book *Chaos* (Gleick, 1988) which contains a suite of Numerator files which demonstrate the butterfly effect, fractals and much more, all of which are described in the accompanying booklet. As the iterative procedures take an exceptionally long time to plot the Mandelbrot Set in Numerator's explicit environment – up to three days – two very fast programs are also included on the disk to provide for investigations into both the Mandelbrot and Julia Sets outside of Numerator.

Naturally enough, even with the fastest procedures, the closer one examines the fractal edges, the longer it takes to decide each pixel's colour. After about six or seven magnifications of any one area, the image begins to break up as the limit of the machine's arithmetic accuracy is reached, but there are many, many hours of fascinating exploring to be done before the need is felt for further enhancements.

[1] P. Hunter, *Order and Chaos – Investigating Non-linear Systems using Numerator* (Logotron/Longman, 1989)

Practicalities

Approaching the Mandelbrot Set, one finds that each wart is a tiny figure shaped much like the parent set. Zooming in for a closer look at one of the tiny figures however, opens up an entirely different pattern: a riot of organic-looking tendrils and curlicules sweeps out in whorls and rows. Magnifying a curlicule reveals yet another scene: it is made up of pairs of whorls joined by bridges of filigree. A magnificent bridge turns out to have two curlicules sprouting from its centre. In the centre of this centre, so to speak, is a four-way bridge with four more curlicules, and in the centre of these curlicules another version of the Mandelbrot Set is found.

The magnified version is not quite the same Mandelbrot Set. As the zoom continues, such objects seem to reappear, but a closer look always turns up differences. Things go on this way forever, infinitely various and frighteningly lovely.

Dewdney, 1985

Almost any microcomputer can produce images similar to those shown in this chapter, given time and, perhaps, the necessity of accepting rather poorer definition. At least one pupil has rewritten one of the simpler BBC BASIC programs for his Sinclair Spectrum and obtained passable results with the small Sinclair sensitised-paper printer. The easiest course of action in school, however, is to obtain a copy of one of the articles quoted and either send for the associated disk or type it in from the listings. Older Acorn machines or those which will emulate BBC BASIC, such as the RM Nimbus, are most common in schools and can use these listings without any changes being necessary. Some facility with programming will of course be necessary if a different dialect of BASIC has to be used. As stressed earlier, by far the best option is to obtain the use of a RISC machine such as an A3000 as it is so much faster. This aids the selection process, and the quality of the results approaches the standard of mainframes not so long ago.

Screen shots are fairly straight forward so long as a reasonably good SLR camera and tripod are available. A high definition colour print film such as Kodacolor Gold 200 or Kodak Ektar 125 is best and it is essential to take the photographs in a darkened room with the screen being the only light source. Maximum aperture will probably be necessary to see what is going on apart from anything else and depth of field is unimportant, but the shutter speed should be $\frac{1}{30}$ second or less, otherwise the scan lines down the screen will spoil the photograph.

Printer screen-dumps vary in flexibility and the user will be limited depending on the combination of computer and printer available. Some of the dumps in this chapter were produced with a BBC Model B computer, Star LC-10 printer and a Computer Concepts *Printmaster* screen-dump ROM. This ROM is very flexible and allows degrees of shading and half tone effects, but the star-commands must be embedded in the program itself. An easier option with the same hardware is to use the *Screenprint* ROM which operates on an interrupt from merely pressing CTRL – P at any stage, but there are no options other than negative. Other dumps shown here were obtained with a 1 megabyte Nimbus PC computer, Panasonic KX-P1081 printer and ILEA's *Print-a-Screen* disk which again is an easy-to-use interrupt routine and works very well in conjunction with LOGO.

Some of the programs quoted offer the option of saving screens to disk, in which case it may be possible to reload them back into a computer graphics package such as Homerton College's *Image* and so be able to subsequently manipulate the picture in a large number of ways and even incorporate it into another design.

Repeated photocopying has already been mentioned, but interesting effects can be obtained by taking a suitable image and progressively photo-enlarging it, possibly in step with zooming into the image itself: the possibilities are endless. Simplified monochrome images can be profitably used for making photo-screens for screen printing; the results can make an interesting parallel with some of the effects produced by tie-and-dye.

Naturally enough, tee-shirts bearing Mandelbrot and Julia Set images are now occasionally available commercially, but an unexpected delight is to discover a knitted pullover on the same theme. Joyce Porteous first displayed it at one of the Mathematical Association's conferences and was soon pressed for copies of the pattern[1].

At the time of writing, relatively little has been done to exploit the 'art side' of fractal graphics. The field is wide open . . .

---

[1] Knitting pattern available from: Joyce Porteous, 115 Wollaton Road, Sheffield S17 4LF or from the Mathematical Association.

9 Plotting Spheres

CHAPTER

Robert Dixon

Introduction

It may be said that both programming and graphics put life into the parts of school mathematics which formal manipulation alone cannot reach. Programming puts a new dynamic power into our play with arithmetic and algebra, while graphics offers endless visual expression to trigonometry and geometry hitherto beyond the scope of artistic means. In my own work I have been fascinated to discover how very much can be achieved in computer graphics with only a smattering of school mathematics, and even less programming knowledge. If you can teach a child to write and read simple formulae it is only a small further step from there to using them in simple programs. Such traditional formal accomplishments at school can now be extended into highly concrete applications. To put this another way: anyone who has succeeded in learning even an average amount of school mathematics has learnt a powerful language for instructing computers to act, to calculate and to draw – with great speed and accuracy.

It is obvious that an important set of links between mathematics and art is at the very heart of computer graphics. Mathematical formulae and geometrical reasoning are the means by which we accomplish the basic image-making techniques of perspective, hidden-line, shading and reflections, as well as object and viewpoint manipulation. In pattern-making, symmetry theory and transformations play the key role. Conversely, graphical output may serve to express mathematical ideas.

This book mainly addresses itself to two groups of readers which may reflect the two directions of exchange described here, namely, art teachers working in an art room and mathematics teachers working in a mathematics room. The computer provides the bridge for a two-way traffic, and because of the way things have originated and developed in schools over the past decade or more, it is more than likely that most school computers are housed in neither the mathematics room nor the art room, but in the computer room. Maybe the neutral territory has its advantages!

The increased opportunity for coursework projects in the GCSE revolution offers an excellent pretext and context for school work in art and mathematics to spill over into the computer room. The spirit of creative investigation fits very well into the task of programming, whose scope for very varied output would be hard to exaggerate. Although ample software packages are available, it is worth stressing the educational merits of the program-it-yourself approach. For, in learning to program even the most simple drawings, the programmer must learn elementary mathematical principles in a thoroughly active way.

The feedback nature of programming brings new dynamics to the learning exercise, increasing the role of, and likelihood of success in, self-tuition:

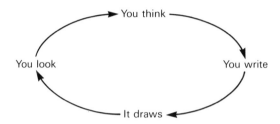

As all programmers know, the process of writing a program progresses with a sequence of illuminating conundra, known as program bugs, which when resolved bring great satisfaction signalled by, in our case, the drawing suddenly going right.

So much for the educational case for programming computer graphics; a word or two now about programming and mathematical skills. The programming need be no higher than novice level, the kind of standard which children are often able to reach largely by self-tuition on a home computer, say, using BASIC. Anyone can learn enough BASIC or other language to write simple programs that will perform substantial tasks. The program commands given in this chapter are in BASIC, but are easily translated to other languages; although, of course, in home and school computing BASIC continues to be by far the most popular programming language. BASIC was devised as a new simplified version of FORTRAN, designed to be a 'formula translator' for all scientific purposes.

The mathematical skills covered in the drawing exercises described in this chapter range from GCSE to middling A-level, and are mostly a matter of traditional school trigonometry. For art teachers who may be more nervous about the mathematics content and initially sceptical of their own abilities I would say: use what you know and learn a little more at a time. It is certainly surprising how much can be drawn using very little mathematics.

Theme and variations

This chapter focuses on the use of simple plotter graphics to draw a variety of patterns upon the surface of a sphere. By so doing, we shall explore some of the marvels in the geometry of the sphere and see in action how coordinates and transformations play a very basic and powerful role in computer graphics.

I have arranged eight separate drawing projects in something of a learning sequence, any or all of which may form the basis of classroom activities. In each I have aimed to supply and to explain the essential formulae. The tasks of writing full programs and of endless and divergent exploration are left to the reader. Mathematics teachers, no doubt, will enjoy checking and developing the formulae for themselves. In each topic I also set a typical problem for readers to puzzle over, or to serve by way of illustration as an indication of the kind of mathematics which go to make up these graphical projects.

Note that computers usually read angular measure (for evaluating sines and arcsines, etc.) in radians, rather than degrees or revolutions. However, it is frequently convenient to think of rotations in terms either of units of revolution or of degrees. Thus, we must live with the frequent need to translate angular units.

$$1 \text{ revolution} = 360° = 2\pi \text{ radians}$$

$\pi = 3.1416$ provides sufficient accuracy for most purposes, but in very exceptional circumstances programmers may be interested to know that $\pi = 3.141\,592\,653\,5\ldots$

It is also useful to be able to think in both Cartesian, (x, y), coordinates and Polar, (r, a), coordinates, and to convert the figures given in one system to figures in the other. This is the essence of sines and cosines.

Plotter graphics consist entirely of straight lines, obtained by means of such commands as MOVE (X, Y) and DRAW (X, Y). Curves are obtained by drawing chains (polygons) of many small line segments.

1 To draw a circle

To plot a circle, plot a sufficiently many-sided regular polygon. Here, in polar coordinates, (r, a), is a BASIC loop for plotting the vertices of a regular fiftygon, to simulate a circle of radius, R, centred on the coordinate origin.

```
INPUT R
MOVEP(R,0)
FOR N=1 TO 50
A=2*PI*N/50
DRAWP(R,A)
NEXT N
```

Polar coordinates provide a natural basis for thinking about regular polygons; however, it is usually necessary and frequently useful to convert polar coordinates, (r, a), to Cartesian coordinates, (x, y). Use:

```
X  =  R*COS(A)
Y  =  R*SIN(A)
```

EXERCISE

1 Derive these conversion formulae from schoolroom definitions of sine and cosine in right-angled triangles.

2 Three dimensions

When working in three dimensions it is convenient to imagine a three-dimensional Cartesian coordinate system, so arranged in your imaginary field of view that you are looking straight down the z-axis towards the x–y plane, with the coordinate origin at the centre of view. For the purposes of perspective drawing, the precise location of the eye on the z-axis is required, but for simplicity's sake we shall, throughout, adopt orthographic perspective, also known as parallel projection. This gives the appearance of things viewed from infinity. Parallels are drawn as parallels and there is no diminution of sizes due to distance. It is a system of perspective used, by the way, in ancient oriental painting as well as modern technical illustration.

To draw an object in orthographic perspective: plot all points (x, y, z) of the object at (x, y) on the drawing plane.

When drawing a sphere centred at $(0, 0, 0)$ you can obtain an effective hidden surface by:

```
IF Z>0 THEN DRAW(X,Y) ELSE MOVE(X,Y)
```

EXERCISE

2 Show by the theorem of Pythagoras that for a sphere centred at $(0, 0)$ with radius r, all points (x, y, z) on its surface satisfy:

$$x^2 + y^2 + z^2 = r^2$$

3 To draw a circle on a sphere

EXERCISE

3 On the surface of a sphere with radius R, a circle is drawn with radius r. Find, in terms of R and r, the distance between the centre of the sphere and the centre of the circle (Pythagoras again).

Suppose your answer to the above question is D. We now consider a program loop which will generate the three-dimensional Cartesian coordinates (x, y, z) of such a circle on a sphere. Let the sphere be centred at $(0, 0, 0)$ and let the circle be centred at $(0, 0, D)$, so that it lies in the plane $z = D$, parallel to the x-y plane and perpendicular to our line of view. In BASIC, let the radius of the circle be R and the radius of the sphere be *RAD*. Here are the vertices of a suitable fiftygon:

```
INPUT  R, RAD
Calculate D
FOR  N  =  0  TO  50
A  =  2 * PI * N / 50
X  =  RAD * COS ( A )
Y  =  RAD * SIN ( A )
Z  =  D
NEXT  N
```

4 Rotations

Rotations about the x-, y- and z-axes provide a convenient way to define positions on a sphere, as well as to obtain all angles of view of the object, so we shall now consider their formulae.

Rotation about the z-axis changes all x and y coordinates but leaves z values unchanged. We consider a positive rotation (which, by mathematical convention, is anticlockwise) about the z-axis by an angle of *ROT* radians. In polar coordinates, all points undergo the simple transformation:

$$(r, a) \longrightarrow (r, a + ROT)$$

Now the rotation about the z-axis gives Cartesian coordinates:

```
NEWX  =  OLDX * COS ( ROT )  -  OLDY * SIN ( ROT )
NEWY  =  OLDX * SIN ( ROT )  +  OLDY * COS ( ROT )
```

Now, consider a similar rotation about the x-axis:

```
NEWY  =  OLDY * COS ( ROT )  -  OLDZ * SIN ( ROT )
NEWZ  =  OLDY * SIN ( ROT )  +  OLDZ * COS ( ROT )
```

and, about the y-axis:

```
NEWX  =  OLDX * COS ( ROT )  -  OLDZ * SIN ( ROT )
NEWZ  =  OLDX * SIN ( ROT )  +  OLDZ * COS ( ROT )
```

EXERCISE

4 Using the well-known formulae for $\sin(A + B)$ etc., derive the above rotation formulae from $(r, a) \rightarrow (r, a + ROT)$.

133

The routine in topic 3 generates points of a circle of radius R on a sphere of radius RAD so that their two centres align with the viewpoint. To relocate such a circle anywhere else on the sphere we need no more than two successive rotations about different axes.

First, rotate each point of the circle (generated by routine 4) about the y-axis. This will displace the circle rightwards from its central starting place. Note that rotations in excess of $\frac{\pi}{2}$ radians take the circle round the back of the sphere.

Second, further rotate each point of the circle about the z-axis, turning it anticlockwise about the viewing axis.

```
INPUT  R , RAD , ROT1 , ROT2
Calculate D
FOR  N  =  0  TO  50

A  =  2 * PI * N / 50
X  =  R * COS ( A )
Y  =  R * SIN ( A )
Z  =  D

NEWX  =  X * COS ( ROT1 ) - Z * SIN ( ROT1 )
NEWZ  =  X * SIN ( ROT1 ) + Z * COS ( ROT1 )
X  =  NEWX
Z  =  NEWZ

NEWX  =  X * COS ( ROT2 ) - Y * SIN ( ROT2 )
NEWY  =  X * SIN ( ROT2 ) + Y * COS ( ROT2 )
X  =  NEWX
Y  =  NEWY

( DRAW / MOVE )   as appropriate

NEXT  N
```

The reader should now experiment with various combined values of *ROT1* and *ROT2*. Circles so displaced about the sphere appear in projection as ellipses, and sufficiently many such circles scattered about the sphere will give a spherical appearance to the drawing.

5 Circles great and small

In the geometry of the sphere, the distinction between great circles and small circles is important. Any circle of radius r lying on a sphere of radius R is a *great circle* of the sphere if and only if $r = R$; otherwise it is a *small circle* of the sphere and $r < R$.

A great circle of a given sphere is any circle having the same radius and centre as the sphere. A great circle lies on the surface of its sphere and bisects it into two hemispheres. And, incidentally, any two great circles of a given sphere bisect each other.

An example of a great circle is the equator on the Earth's globe. The circles of longitude are also all great circles of the Earth's globe; whereas all the circles of latitude except the equator are small circles. (In star gazing, the annual zodiacal path of the Sun among the fixed stars, called the ecliptic, is a great circle of, and fixed upon, the celestial sphere; while the viewer's (ideal) horizon is a slowly but constantly rotating great circle of the celestial sphere.)

EXERCISE

5 Plot a sphere covered with numerous and randomly orientated great circles. ('A ball of string'.)

The centres of small circles of a given sphere lie below its surface. In exercise 3 we worked out the distance between the centres of a sphere and a small circle of the sphere in terms of both of their radii (R and r).

We have already mentioned that circles of geographical latitude are small circles of the Earth's globe, as are all circles on a sphere which are not great. Crater rims on a moon approximate to small circles of the moon's globe. (Stargazing again: the daily path of the Sun about the viewer is a small circle of the viewer's sphere of view – except on the days of Spring and Autumn Equinox, when it performs a great circle.)

Note that a given circle can be great only to one sphere but small to infinitely many.

6 Longitudes and latitudes

The familiar geographical coordinate system of longitudes and latitudes is based upon the polar axis of the Earth's daily rotation. Every point P on the Earth's surface is given uniquely by a pair of angles (longitude, latitude). The first of these angles ($0° \leqslant$ longitude $\leqslant 360°$) measures the rotation about the north–south axis from the Greenwich Meridian to the meridian of P; while the second angle ($-90° \leqslant$ latitude $\leqslant 90°$) measures the meridian arc from P to the Equator. By learning to draw a longitude–latitude grid on a sphere we are learning about an entirely general and highly useful principle: spherical coordinates.

Start by imagining the globe of radius, *RAD*, in an initial location, for example, centred at $(0, 0, 0)$ with north and south poles at $(0, RAD, 0)$ and $(0, -RAD, 0)$ respectively. Next, write a program to generate the longitudes and latitudes in this initial location. Finally, obtain various views of the longitude–latitude spherical grid by rotations as discussed in topic 4.

Longitudes

To generate the points of the circle of longitude, *LONG*, generate the points of the great circle of the sphere lying in the *x–y* plane and rotate it about the *y*-axis through an angle of *LONG*. Repeat this for various values of *LONG*, for example, let $LONG = 0, 15, 30, \ldots, 345°$.

```
FOR  C  =  0  TO  11

LONG  =  2 * P I * C / 2 4

FOR  N  =  0  TO  50

A  =  2 * P I * N / 5 0
X  =  R A D * C O S ( A )
Y  =  R A D * S I N ( A )
Z  =  0

NEWX  =  X * C O S ( L O N G ) - Z * S I N ( L O N G )
NEWZ  =  X * S I N ( L O N G ) + X * C O S ( L O N G )
X  =  N E W X
Z  =  N E W Z
```

(followed by view rotations)

```
NEXT  N

NEXT  C
```

EXERCISE

6 What is the radius of a circle of latitude *LAT* on a sphere of radius *RAD*?

Latitudes

Suppose your answer to exercise 6 is *R*, and its *y*-coordinate is *D* as calculated in exercise 3, then the points of latitude *LAT* are generated as the circle of radius *R*, centred at $(0, D, 0)$ and lying in the plane $y = D$. Repeat for various values of *LAT*.

```
FOR  C  =  -6  TO  6

LAT  =  PI*C/12
Calculate R
Calculate D
FOR  N  =  0  TO  50
A  =  2*PI*N/50
X  =  R*COS(A)
Z  =  R*SIN(A)
Y  =  D
```

(followed by view rotations)

```
NEXT  N

NEXT  C
```

7 Spherical symmetries

This topic is concerned with the geometric basis for designing symmetry patterns on a sphere, which Euclid studied by way of the Platonic solids, and which in prehistoric Scotland were carved in granite balls, known as miniliths (see Figure 1).

Figure 1 'Minilith'. One of several thousand prehistoric carved stone balls found in Scotland that exhibit spherical symmetries, purpose and precise origin unknown. This one, known as the Cowie Stone, shows tetrahedral symmetry
Courtesy of the National Museum of Scotland

Suppose you wish to divide the surface of a sphere into a finite number of identical parts: in what ways can this be done? The answer to this question corresponds to the list of possible symmetry groups of the sphere.

All symmetry groups of the sphere involve only rotations and/or reflections. We approach the problem by considering rotational symmetry in isolation, and complete the story later with the addition of reflection. There are just four possible varieties of rotational symmetry of the sphere, each determined by the number and relative disposition of the axes. We have already encountered the simplest variety in the previous topic of drawing grids of latitude and longitude, namely, one axis. We shall now look at the other three varieties. Each has several simultaneous axes of rotational symmetry and corresponds to the symmetry of one or other of the five Platonic solids (regular polyhedra), namely, cube, octahedron, tetrahedron and dodecahedron, icosahedron.

To understand these symmetries we can proceed as follows: imagine that our sphere circumscribes a chosen Platonic solid, and look accordingly for the locations of its set of rotational symmetry axes. They connect opposite pairs of vertices and the pairs of centres of both opposite faces and opposite edges, and it is an easy matter to see their rotational periods.

Cube–octahedral symmetry

The cube and octahedron are duals (the face centres of each forming the vertices of the other) and so have the same groups of symmetries. In all there are 24 symmetry rotations to be found:

1 3 mutually perpendicular axes of period 4: connecting centres of opposite faces of the cube and opposite vertices of the octahedron.
2 4 axes of period 3: connecting centres of opposite faces of the octahedron and opposite vertices of the cube.
3 6 axes of period 2: connecting the centres of opposite edges in both cube and octahedron.

Any figure on the surface of a sphere which is transformed from its initial location by each of these 24 rotations in turn will create a spherical symmetry pattern of period 24. It is convenient to align the three period-4 axes with the x-, y- and z-axes, making it an easier matter to find the locations of the other axes.

Note that the formulae for rotations given in topic 4 apply only to rotations about the x-, y- and z-axes. Rotations about other axes, however, may be achieved by a product of x-, y- and/or z-rotations. The rules for finding the single rotation which is equivalent to a given combination of two rotations present an interesting puzzle-project, but I shall provide here a list of the required 24 rotations of the cube–octahedral symmetry group.

Adopting the notation $x(\alpha)$ to denote a rotation of angle α about the x-axis, and £ to mean 'followed by', the list is:

$z(360N/4)$ £ $x(360M/4)$
$z(360N/4)$ £ $y(90)$
$z(360N/4)$ £ $y(270)$

with N and M independently $= 0, 1, 2, 3$.

Icosa–dodecahedral symmetry

The icosahedron and dodecahedron are dual solids and share the same group of symmetry transformations:

1 6 axes of period 5: connecting centres of opposite faces of the dodecahedron or opposite vertices of the icosahedron.
2 10 axes of period 3: connecting centres of opposite faces of the icosahedron or opposite vertices of the dodecahedron.
3 15 axes of period 2: connecting the centres of opposite edges of either icosahedron or dodecahedron.

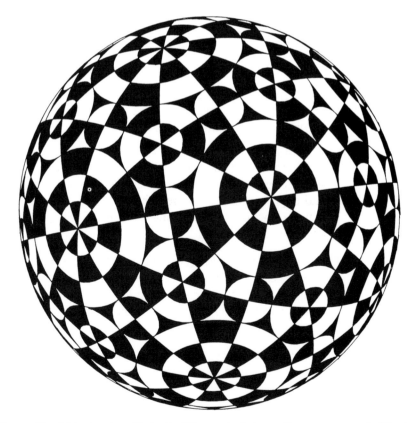

Figure 2   This drawing, 'Spherical Symmetry' shows the arrangement of the two-fold, three-fold and five-fold axes in the pattern of icosa-dodecahedral symmetry

This makes 60 symmetry rotations in all (counting identity):

$z(360N/5)$
$z(360N/5)$ £ $x(180)$
$z(360/10 + 360N/5)$ £ $x(63.43)$ £ $z(360M/5)$
$z(360/10 + 360N/5)$ £ $x(116.57)$ £ $z(360M/5)$

with N and M independently $= 0, 1, 2, 3, 4$.

Any figure drawn on a sphere and moved from its initial location by each of these 60 rotations in turn will generate a pattern of spherical symmetry with period 60. (See Figure 3.)

Figure 3 'Men on a Sphere'

EXERCISE

7 Given that the angle between faces of a tetrahedron is $70.53°$, formulate the 12 rotations in the tetrahedral symmetry group.

Mirror symmetries

Each of the rotational symmetry groups can be extended by including reflection, the order doubling in each case. Taking the icosa-dodecahedral symmetry as our example, there are 15 planes of mirror symmetry to be found in the dodecahedron. These planes cut the sphere into hemispheres whose poles are the 15 antipodal pairs of period 2 rotacentres. The great circles of the sphere cut by these planes divide its surface into 120 congruent right-angled triangles.

The additional 30 transformations introduced by the inclusion of reflection into icosa-dodecahedral symmetry are formulated by combining each of the 30 rotations in turn with *point reflection* in the sphere's centre:

$$(x, y, z) \longrightarrow (-x, -y, -z)$$

The same result can be achieved by combining each of the 30 rotations in turn with one of the 15 plane reflections, say

$$(x, y, z) \longrightarrow (-x, y, z)$$

The 15 plane reflections correspond to the combinations of point reflection with the 15 half-turns.

Escher-like tessellations of the sphere can be devised by considering 60 fundamental regions of the sphere involving only rotational symmetry. Take any pair of mirror image triangles from the 120 formed by the above 15 great circles. Now distort the boundaries in a manner entirely analogous to that for plane tessellation described in Chapter 6.

8 Spherical phyllotaxis

This diversion into the relation between plant geometry and the golden ratio is as fascinating as it is instructive.

How can you distribute N (say 100) equal small circles over the surface of a sphere so that they are optimally spaced or packed?
Answer: do what plants do – arrange spirally at regular angular intervals of the golden angle

$$GA = 2\pi\tau \text{ radians} = 222.49°$$

where τ is the well known golden ratio given by

$$\tau = \frac{1}{\tau + 1}, \text{ that is, } \tau = 0.618\,033\,9\ldots$$

Phyllotaxis literally means 'leaf-arrangement', but the geometry of its solutions applies to any repetitive parts of plants: buds, branches, thorns, florets and fruits. Despite the enormous variety of plant forms, nearly all of them demonstrate the spatial economy of just a handful of geometric possibilities. Besides certain examples of bilateral and point symmetries, the most ubiquitous tendency in plants is the spiral succession described above.

Botanists call the angle of spiral succession, say, of buds on a stem, the *divergence* and it has long been known that in plants divergence tends to be equal to *GA*.

What the plants are telling us, so to speak, is of the existence of an optimal packing/spacing angle in spirals or helices. Number theory can be invoked to explain why all other values of divergence give less economical results. The same patterns can be found in globe form, our present concern, such as in the spherical arrangement of the 'fairies' on a dandelion clock (seed head) as in Figure 4.

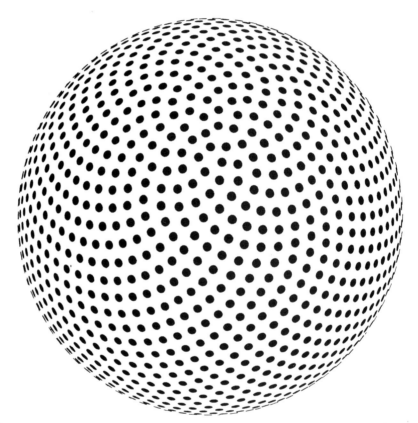

Figure 4 'Spherical Phyllotaxis'. A sequence of equal circles spaced/packed evenly on the surface of a sphere

0.618 033 ... has been turning up in mathematics and science since time immemorial, and there are frequent claims for its relevance to art. It was Leonardo da Vinci who first called it the 'golden' ratio. Kepler had called it a 'jewel', while reserving the title of 'gold' for the theorem of Pythagoras. The Greeks, who focused considerable attention upon its place in geometry, called it the 'extreme and mean ratio' and defined it geometrically as the cut C made in a line segment AB so that the ratio of large part to small part equals whole to large, see Figure 5.

Figure 5 Golden section of a line segment: $\dfrac{CB}{AC} = \dfrac{AB}{CB}$

The circumference of a circle can be cut into two parts bearing the golden ratio in analogous fashion, in which case the angle subtended at its centre by the larger of the two arcs is $GA = 0.618\,034 \times 360°$.

Note that the complementary angle, $360 - GA$, can be used as the golden angle to the same effect as GA except for reversing the sense of spiral rotation. $360 - GA = 360\tau^2 = 137.51°$ and is well served in radians by the approximation of 2.4.

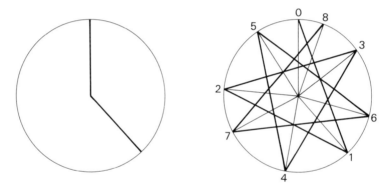

Figure 6 The golden angle and successive rotations

So much, for the moment, for divergence. We next tackle the problem of formulating a spiral which proceeds to 'enclose' the surface of a sphere at constant rate. The equivalent problem for a plane spiral is solved by Fermat's spiral $R = \sqrt{A}$. To solve the spherical problem, consider the following.

EXERCISE

8 **(a)** For a sphere of radius R, find, in terms of *LAT*, the area of the north polar cap bounded by latitude *LAT*.

(b) Express your answer to (a) as a fraction of the whole surface.

The answers to exercise 8 provide the basis for programming 'spherical phyllotaxis' (see Figure 4, p. 142).

```
FOR  C  =  0  TO  N
```

Draw small circle centred at $(LAT, LONG) = \left[ASN\left(1 - \frac{2C}{N}\right), C \times GA \right]$, where ASN means arcsine

```
NEXT  C
```

Having successfully drawn spherical phyllotaxis, the reader should experiment with various values of divergence other than *GA*.

When thinking about the effects produced by drawing phyllotaxis patterns with divergence it is helpful to consider what happens when the divergence has a rational value. That is to say, let divergence $= \frac{p}{q}$ revolution, where p and q are whole numbers (and for practical purposes not too large): the result is a pattern of small circles arranged on q circles of longitude. By contrast, when the value of divergence is irrational (say, $\frac{1}{\pi}$ revolution $= 2$ radians), no two of the small circles can appear on the same longitude, and instead we find them arranged on spirals whose numbers correspond to the denominators of close rational approximations. The strong tendency to golden angle divergence in plants was originally discovered through this connection between geometry and number theory. By counting such spirals of alignments in pinecones, pineapples, sunflowers, daisies, and so on, we frequently find them to be Fibonacci numbers:

$$1, 1, 2, 3, 5, 8, 13, 21, 34, 55, \ldots$$

$$\left(F_0 = 0, F_1 = 1, \text{ and } F_n = F_{n-2} + F_{n-1} : \quad \frac{F_{n-1}}{F_n} \longrightarrow \tau \text{ as } n \text{ increases.} \right)$$

Conclusion

In this chapter I have pursued a set of exercises in computer drawing, which take as their main linking theme the geometry of the sphere, and which grow from simple beginnings towards various sophisticated blossomings. My chosen subject was, of course, highly specific; but it has provided the opportunity to deal in practical detail with some of the most fundamental mathematical devices for programming graphics, namely coordinates and transformations. I hope also to have illustrated something of the general proposition that computer graphics is a marvellous means to linking art and mathematics. Figures 7 and 8 show an extension of these ideas.

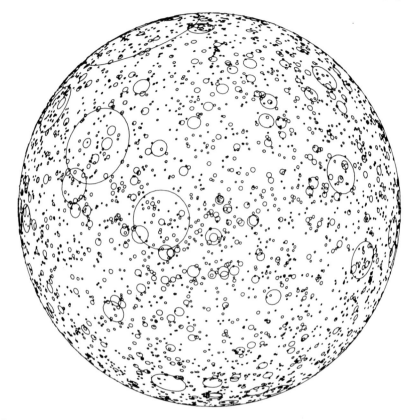

Figure 7 'Moon'. Circles of random size and random location on the surface of a sphere

Needless to say, many another theme, and/or other kinds of graphical output, might be chosen for classroom activities. In recent years, for example, fractals, chaos and iterations have proved very popular themes with a dazzling output of imagery. Moreover, whatever the theme there nearly always seems to be an opportunity to link both art and mathematics with our interest in and appreciation of nature.

What I have not attempted to describe is the actual process of a computer project. From a learner's or teacher's point of view, there are numerous cognitive aspects of programming which contrast strongly with traditional written exercises. Apart from the important roles played by feedback and visual output, which I mentioned in my introduction, there is an almost unavoidable potential in programming to build upon one's simple beginnings, in a step-by-step manner. Energy is concentrated on one concept or problem at a time. Today's simple working programs can become the bricks for building tomorrow's more sophisticated programs. The process can be guided or allowed to unfold as a spontaneous act of discovery. It extends over time almost indefinitely and presents endless points of creative departure on the way.

Figure 8 'Inversion'. The inversion of a plane about a centre not in that plane is a sphere. The inversion of a sphere about a centre on the sphere is a plane

References and Bibliography

K. Albarn et al, *The Language of Pattern* (Thames and Hudson, London, 1974)

K. Albarn & J. Miall-Smith, *Diagram* (Thames and Hudson, London, 1977)

I. O. Angell, *A Practical Introduction to Computer Graphics* (Macmillan, 1981)

N. Ardalun & L. Bakhtiar, *The Sense of Unity* (University of Chicago Press, 1973)

Arts Council, *Art in Revolution: Soviet Art and Design since 1917* (Arts Council, 1971)

C. Athey, *Parental Involvement in Nursery Education, in Early Childhood*, Vol. 1, No. 3 (December 1980)

J. K. Backhouse, 'Fractal patterns on a Square', *Mathematics in School* (May 1986)

J. Bourgoin, *Arabic Geometrical Pattern and Design* (Dover, New York, 1973)

B. Brookes, 'An Introduction to J. Sauvy and M. Sauvy', *The Child's Discovery of Space* (Penguin, 1974)

J. S. Bruner, *The Process of Educaton* (Harvard University Press, 1960)

R. Buckminster Fuller, *Synergetics* (Macmillan, New York, 1975)

T. Burckhardt, *Sacred Art in East and West* (Perennial Books, London, 1967)

M. Cook, 'Fun with Fractals', *Micro User* (July 1989)

H. S. M. Coxeter, *Regular Polytopes* (Macmillan, London, 1963)

K. Crennel, 'Mandelbrot Graphics', *BEEBUG* (May 1986)

K. Critchlow, *Order in Space* (Thames & Hudson, 1969)

K. Critchlow, *Islamic Pattern* (Schocken Books, New York, 1976)

H. M. Cundy & A. P. Rollett, *Mathematical Models* (Oxford University Press, 1961)

DES, *Mathematics for Ages 5 to 16* (HMSO, 1988)

DES, *Design and Technology for Ages 5 to 16* (HMSO, 1989)

K. Devlin, 'Futures: Microguardian', *The Guardian* (4 July 1985)

A. K. Dewdney, 'Computer Recreations', *Scientific American* (August 1985)

A. K. Dewdney, 'Computer Recreations', *Scientific American* (November 1987)

A. K. Dewdney, *The Armchair Universe* (W. H. Freeman, 1988)

R. Dixon, *Mathographics* (Basil Blackwell, 1987)

G. Eilenberger, *Catalogue for the Goethe–Institut Exhibition, 'Frontiers of Chaos'* (1985)

I. El-Said & A. Parman, *Geometric Concepts in Islamic Art* (The World of Islam Festival Trust and Scorpion Publishing Ltd, 1988)

B. Ernst, *The Magic Mirror of M. C. Escher* (Tarquin, 1985)

M. C. Escher, *The graphic work of M. C. Escher* (Oldbourne Press, 1961)

M. C. Escher, *Giftwraps by Artists: M. C. Escher* (Abrams, New York, 1987)

A. Fedonczuk, 'Mandelbrots in Moments', *Acorn User* (March 1988)

R. Gelman & C. R. Gallistel, 'The Child's Understanding of Number', *Early Child Development and Education* ed. M. Donaldson, R. Grieve, C. Pratt (Basil Blackwell, 1983)

M. Ghyka, *The Geometry of Art and Life* (Sheed & Ward, New York, 1946)

J. Gleick, *Chaos* (Heinemann, 1988)

C. Gray, *The Great Experiment: Russian Art 1863–1922* (Thames and Hudson, 1962)

H. Gresty & J. Lewison (eds), *Constructivism in Poland 1923–36* (Kettle's Yard Gallery in association with Museum Sztuki, Lodz, 1983)

J. Howse, *Maths or Magic* (Watkins, London, 1976)

D. Johnson-Davies, 'Join the Mandelbrot Set', *Acorn User* (May 1986)

I. Kant, *Critique of Judgement*, trans. J. Haden (Bobbs-Merrill, New York, 1965)

P. Klee, *Notebooks, Volume One: The Thinking Eye* (Lund Humphries, London, 1961)

Le Corbusier, *The Modulor*, trans. P. de Francia and A. Bostock (Faber and Faber, London, 1961)

E. Levinger, 'The Theory of Hungarian Constructivism', *The Art Bulletin*, Vol. LXIX, Number 3 (September 1987)

J. L. Locher, *Escher, with a Complete Catalogue of the Graphic Works* (Thames and Hudson, 1982)

N. McAdoo, 'Aesthetic Education and the "Antimony on Taste"', *British Journal of Aesthetics*, Vol. 27, No. 4 (Autumn 1987)

B. B. Mandelbrot, *The Fractal Beauty of Nature* (W. H. Freeman, 1982)

R. W. Marks, *The Dymaxion World of Buckminster Fuller* (Reinhold, New York, 1960)

D. Marr, *Vision: A Computational Investigation into the Human Representation and Processing of Visual Information* (W. H. Freeman, 1982)

Mathematical Association, *132 Short Programs for the Mathematics Classroom* (Stanley Thornes, 1985)

J. Matthews, 'Children drawing: are young children really scribbling?' *Early Child Development and Care*, Vol. 18 (Gordon and Breach, 1984)

J. Matthews, 'The young child's early representation and drawing', *Early Childhood Education: A Developmental Curriculum*, ed. G. Blenkin & A. V. Kelly (Paul Chapman, 1988)

J. Matthews, 'How young children give meaning to drawing', *Pictures at an Exhibition*, ed. T. Dalley & A. Gilroy (Routledge, 1989)

J. Matthews, 'Expression, Representation and Drawing in Early Childhood' (University of London Doctoral thesis, 1990)

J. Matthews, 'The genesis of aesthetic sensibility', *Drawing, Art and Development*, ed. D. Thistlewood (N.S.E.A.D. and Routledge, 1990a)

R. Meager, 'Aesthetic Concepts', *British Journal of Aesthetics*, Vol. 10 (October 1970)

A. Nakov, *Avante-Garde Russe* (Art Data, 1986)

S. H. Nasr, *An Introduction to Islamic Cosmological Doctrine* (Harvard University Press, Massachusetts, 1964)

R. Noss, 'Fractals, Turtles and Snowflakes', *Micromath*, Vol. 1, No. 1 (Association of Teachers of Mathematics, 1985)

A. Paccard, *Traditional Islamic Craft in Moroccan Architecture*, Vol. 1 (Saint-Jorioz-Editions Atelier 74, 1980)

R. Padwick, & T. Walker, *Pattern: Its Structure and Geometry* (Sunderland Arts Centre, 1977)

W. A. Phillips, S. B. Hobbs & F. R. Pratt, 'Intellectual realism in children's drawing of cubes', *Cognition*, **6** (1978)

J. Piaget & B. Inhelder, *The Child's Conception of Space* (Routledge and Kegan Paul, 1956)

H. Pietgen & P. Richter, *The Beauty of Fractals* (Springer-Verlag, 1986)

E. R. Ranucci, *Creating Escher Type Drawings* (Creative Publications, California, 1977)

W. W. Sawyer, *Prelude to Mathematics* (Penguin, 1955)

R. Scruton, *Art and Imagination* (Methuen, London, 1974)

V. Sekules (Ed.), *The University of East Anglia Collection* (University of East Anglia, 1984)

F. Sibley, 'Aesthetic Concepts', *Philosophy Looks at the Arts*, ed. J. Margolis (Charles Scribner's Sons, New York, 1962)

N. R. Smith, *Experience and Art: Teaching Children to Paint* (Teachers College Press, Columbia University, 1983)

P. Stevens, *Patterns in Nature* (Penguin, 1974)

R. Stites, *Revolutionary Dreams: Utopian visions and experimental life in the Russian Revolution* (Oxford University Press, 1989)

R. Taylor, 'Understanding the Mandelbrot Set with A-level students', *Micromath*, Vol. 2, No. 2 (1986)

L. Thomas, *The Lives of a Cell* (Viking Press, USA, 1974)

D'Arcy Thompson, *On Growth and Form* (Cambridge University Press, 1917)

P. Vitruvius, *Ten Books on Architecture*, trans. by M. N. Morgan (Dover, New York, 1960)

H. Weyl, *Symmetry* (Princeton University Press, Princeton, 1952)

T. Wilkie, 'Maths experts attack repetitive learning', *The Independent* (15 Feb 1988)

J. Willats, 'How children learn to draw realistic pictures', pp. 367–82, *Quarterly Journal of Experimental Psychology*, **29** (1977)

J. Willats, 'What do the marks in the picture stand for? The child's acquisition of systems of transformation and denotation', *Review of Research in Visual Arts Education*, **13** (1981)

J. Willats, 'Drawing systems revisited: the role of denotation systems in children's figure drawings', *Visual Order: The Nature and Development of Pictorial Representation*, ed. N. H. Freeman & M. V. Cox (Cambridge University Press, 1985)

E. Wilson, *Islamic Designs* (British Museum Publications, 1988)

D. Wolf & C. Fucigna, 'Representation before picturing'. Transcript of presentation at Symposium on Drawing Development, British Psychological Society International Conference on 'Psychology and the Arts' (University of Cardiff, 1983)

W. Wynne Willson, *The Mathematics Curriculum: Geometry* (Blackie, 1977)

Index